New Readers Press

D1290981

ReadingWise

Comprehension Strategies That Work

8

Series Consultant

Diane J. Sawyer, Ph.D.
Murfree Professor of Dyslexic Studies
Middle Tennessee State University

ReadingWise 8: Comprehensive Strategies That Work
ISBN 1-56420-332-8
Copyright © 2003 New Readers Press
New Readers Press
U.S. Publishing Division of Laubach Literacy
1320 Jamesville Avenue, Syracuse, New York 13210

Printed in the United States of America
9 8 7 6 5 4 3 2 1

All proceeds from the sale of New Readers Press materials
support literacy programs in the United States and worldwide.

Developer: Kraft & Kraft, New York, NY
Series Editor: Judi Lauber
Production Director: Heather Witt
Designer: Shelagh Clancy
Illustrations: Linda Tiff, Brian Wallace, James P. Wallace
Production Specialist: Jeffrey R. Smith
Cover Design: Kimbrly Koennecke

Contents

Introduction   **To the Student** 5

Vocabulary   Lesson 1 ◆ **Using Clues to Meaning** 6
Using Context Clues

**Reading
Strategies**   Lesson 2 ◆ **Getting Ready to Read** 9
Predicting Content; Setting a Purpose and Method

Lesson 3 ◆ **Thinking as You Read** 12
Questioning the Text; Monitoring Comprehension

Lesson 4 ◆ **Reflecting After You Read** 15
Summarizing and Paraphrasing

**Topic and
Main Idea**   Lesson 5 ◆ **Using the Writer's Point** 18
Using the Topic and Main Idea

Details   Lesson 6 ◆ **Using Important Details** 21
Understanding the Significance of Details

Sequence   Lesson 7 ◆ **Using Time Order** 24
Understanding Sequence

**Cause and
Effect**   Lesson 8 ◆ **Using Reasons** 27
Understanding Cause and Effect

Classification   Lesson 9 ◆ **Using Groups** 30
Understanding Classification

**Comparison/
Contrast**   Lesson 10 ◆ **Using Like and Unlike** 33
Understanding Comparison and Contrast

Outcomes   Lesson 11 ◆ **Using Predictions** 36
Applying Predictions of Outcome

Conclusions   Lesson 12 ◆ **Using Clear Thinking** 39
Applying Conclusions

Inferences   Lesson 13 ◆ **Filling Gaps** 42
Making Inferences

Lesson 14 ◆ **Using Good Guesses** 45
Applying Inferences

Generalizations   Lesson 15 ◆ **Getting the Big Picture** **48**
                                  Making Generalizations

                       Lesson 16 ◆ **Checking the Big Picture** **51**
                                  Testing Generalizations

Facts and   Lesson 17 ◆ **Finding Facts and Opinions** **54**
Opinions   *Separating Fact from Opinion*

Evaluating   Lesson 18 ◆ **Checking the Facts** **57**
                                  Evaluating Statements of Fact

                       Lesson 19 ◆ **Thinking about Opinions** **60**
                                  Evaluating Opinions

                       Lesson 20 ◆ **Thinking About the Author** **63**
                                  Evaluating an Author's Viewpoint, Purpose, and Bias

                                  ***ReadingWise* Strategies** **66**
                                  Summary Chart

                                  Answer Key **68**

To the Student

Welcome to *ReadingWise 8*. This book will help you understand and remember more of what you read.

Good readers think when they read. This book is about the thinking skills they use.

Life has already taught you a wide range of thinking skills. This book will show you how to use them for reading.

ReadingWise 8 has 20 lessons. Each lesson builds one skill and has four parts:

- This Is the Idea tells what skill you will learn.
- Take a Closer Look shows how to use the skill.
- Try It helps you use the skill.
- Use It lets you use the skill on your own.

Adults need to read many things every day. This book includes
- workplace memos
- rules and directions
- how-to tips
- news and sports reports
- charts and graphs
- editorials, opinion columns, and letters to the editor
- ads
- tables of contents
- texts in history, science, nature, and language
- and other things

As you read these things, *ReadingWise* helps you practice thinking skills. And the skills help you become a better reader.

Using Clues to Meaning

A writer may define a word in the text or use a synonym to explain it. Other clues in the text, combined with what you know, may help you guess what a word means. These are all *context clues,* or hints that help you figure out a word's meaning.

This Is the Idea

Read this part of a science text and decide what the words in blue ink mean.

The Sponge of the Desert

The state flower of Arizona is a cactus, the stately saguaro, which grows so tall that it resembles a tree with few branches and no leaves. If you look closely at the saguaro's stem, you will see that it is fluted, like some columns on buildings. Vertical indentations run the length of the stem. The depth of these valleys, or flutes, varies from time to time because the pulp within the saguaro's stem can expand like a sponge to hold water. When the pulp is well saturated, it bulges outward, the entire stem becomes distended, and the flutes become shallower. On the other hand, when the pulp becomes desiccated during a long dry spell, the entire stem draws inward and the flutes become deeper. This ability to function as a living water tank serves the saguaro well in the arid conditions of its desert habitat.

You may not know the words *fluted, vertical indentations,* or *flutes,* but clues in the passage can help you guess their meanings.

The writer says that flutes are valleys, so you know that a flute must be a kind of low trench between higher ridges. The writer also says that the vertical indentations "run the length of the stem." Therefore, you know that these vertical indentations are trenches running up and down the stem of the saguaro cactus.

Now you can make a good guess at the meaning of *fluted.* You read that the fluted stem, "like some columns on buildings," has vertical indentations or flutes. Therefore, *fluted* means "having trenches that run up and down its length."

In a similar way, you can guess the meanings of *distended* and *desiccated.* The writer says that when the stem is distended, it bulges outward and the flutes become shallower. From this, you can guess that *distended* means "swollen." Because the writer then says "On the other hand," you can guess that *desiccated* means something opposite to *distended.* You read that the pulp becomes desiccated during a dry spell and the stem draws inward. So you can guess that *desiccated* means "dried out and shrunken."

Take a Closer Look

Read this part of a business text and look for context clues.

Is a Franchise Right for You?

Some people who want to start a small business may feel not quite ready to go it alone. A franchise may be a good compromise between the risks and freedom of total independence and the security of working for someone else. A franchise is an agreement between a large company—the franchisor—and a small-business operator—the franchisee. The parties enter into a reciprocal agreement. The franchisor allows the use of the company's brands and sale of its goods and services. In return, the franchisee pays a franchise fee and sometimes other expenses. The franchisee also allows the franchisor to stipulate rules and procedures for running the business.

Typically, the franchisee benefits from the franchisor's advertising and marketing, management training, and sometimes financing. Often the franchisor helps the franchisee find a location for the business. In turn, the franchisor gets ongoing royalties and advertising fees from the franchisee. The company also benefits from having an exclusive wholesale market for its goods and services. The franchisee is usually required to buy from the franchisor and enjoined from buying from other companies.

In general, for the franchisee, the experience is not like starting a business from scratch. It's like opening a branch of a business that is already successful.

Look for context clues such as these:

- A rash act is hasty or reckless.

- a rash act, which is a hasty or reckless one

- a rash, or hasty, act

- rash, hasty, reckless,

- the rash—reckless—act

- It's best to gather all the information and then take time to think, rather than make a rash decision.

Write your answers.

1. Judging from context clues, what is a compromise?

   _____

2. Judging from context clues, what is a franchisor?

   _____

3. Judging from context clues, what is a franchisee?

   _____

4. Judging from context clues, what is a reciprocal agreement?

   _____

5. Judging from context clues, what does *stipulate* mean?

   _____

6. Judging from context clues, what does *enjoined* mean?

   _____

Try It

Read this part of a civics text and look for context clues.

According to a Recent Poll . . .

At election time, it's hard to listen to any news report without hearing the results of a public-opinion poll. Many people are skeptical about the accuracy of polls, but pollsters wave their doubts aside. They aver that polling techniques can predict, based on a relatively minuscule sample, what the population as a whole is likely to do.

George Gallup, a pioneer of modern polling and sampling techniques, is said to have compared his methods to tasting soup. A person needs to stir the soup well. Then, a sample of a single spoonful will be sufficient to determine whether the whole bowl needs salt.

For pollsters, the equivalent of stirring the soup is making sure that the sample is characteristic of the whole population. They don't want to sample an atypical group like an isolated salty spot. They make sure of this by making the sample as random as possible. Trying to find people who are "average" doesn't work.

School Budget: Too Close To Call

For 40%
Against 37%
Undecided 23%

Write your answers on separate paper.

1. Judging from context clues, what does *skeptical* mean?
2. Judging from context clues, what does *aver* mean?
3. Judging from context clues, what does *minuscule* mean?
4. Judging from context clues, what does *sufficient* mean?
5. Judging from context clues, what does *atypical* mean?

Use It

Read this list of departments in a large store. Each is followed by the name of an item found in that department.

Housewares . . . . frying pan
Pharmacy . . . . cough drops
Lingerie . . . . nightgown
Stationery . . . . envelopes
Electronics . . . . television
Cosmetics . . . . lipstick

Using the listed item as a clue, guess what each department name means. Write your answers on separate paper.

Walk around a large department store. Is there a department name that you don't understand? Take a look at the items in the department. Do they give you a clue to what the name means?

Getting Ready to Read

Predicting Content; Setting a Purpose and Method

This Is the Idea

Why and how would you read this special issue of a magazine?

THRIFTY DRIVER
Special Issue

SMALL REPAIRS, BIG SAVINGS

If it has been a while since you last did routine maintenance on your car, you'll be glad that you read this special issue. It will help you keep your car running at its best and most economical.

Your Tuneup Checklist 8
Will Your Muffler Hold Up? 11
Little Repairs That You Should Make Right Now 19
Don't Let Your Brakes Let You Down 23
How Good Are Your Tires? 27
Replacing Your Windshield Wipers 33

> **Before you start to read, skim the text to get an idea of what it's about. Look for titles, headings, and key words. Then think about *why* and *how* you will read.**

The name of the magazine, the special issue announcement, and the titles of the articles tell you that the topic is how to keep a car in good condition. The key words in blue ink all relate to repairs and maintenance.

How you would read articles in this magazine depends on why you were reading. Sometimes you read quickly to get just certain information or to get a general idea. At other times, you read slowly to get information in depth or to understand more detailed ideas and concepts.

Why would someone read the article "Your Tuneup Checklist" quickly before going on to another?

    a. to learn how a car's engine operates

    b. to find out what tasks are part of a tuneup

The second choice, b, is better. If you wanted to get just a quick idea of what should be done during a tuneup, you would skim the article quickly.

On the other hand, if you had noticed that your brakes were screeching, you might be concerned enough to read "Don't Let Your Brakes Let You Down" very carefully.

Take a Closer Look

Decide why and how you would read various parts of this news report.

What to do

- Skim the text, using titles, headings, and key words to help you decide what the topic is.

- Think about why and how you will read.

- If you want to understand something in depth, read slowly.

- If you want to find certain facts or get a general idea, read quickly.

- If you want to help yourself remember, take notes.

City Votes Tomorrow

SOUTHWEST CITY — Southwest City voters go to the polls tomorrow to vote in what experts are predicting will be the closest mayoral election in a decade.

Polling Hours

Election officials have extended polling hours across the city, responding to criticism following the last election. To accommodate people with unusual work schedules, polls will open at 6:00 AM and remain open until 9:00 PM. Anyone in line at closing time will be permitted to vote.

Polling Places

In addition to extending polling hours, election officials have added a dozen new polling places across the city. This change is part of an effort to reduce crowding and end the long lines that have characterized past elections. (*See map of polling places on page 12.*)

A Long, Hard Campaign

This campaign has been one of the most sharply contested in memory, with charges and countercharges made by all candidates. A key issue has been the question of fundraising.

In addition to extending polling hours, election officials have

Write your answers.

1. What purpose might you have for reading this entire report from beginning to end?

   _____

2. What purpose might you have for turning to page 12 before reading any further?

   _____

3. You have heard rumors about improper fundraising by one candidate. Which part of the report will you read carefully to help you judge whether those rumors are true?

   _____

4. For what reason might you stop reading after the section called "Polling Hours" and feel that you didn't need to read more?

   _____

Try It

Look at this table of contents. Decide why and how you would read chapters of this book.

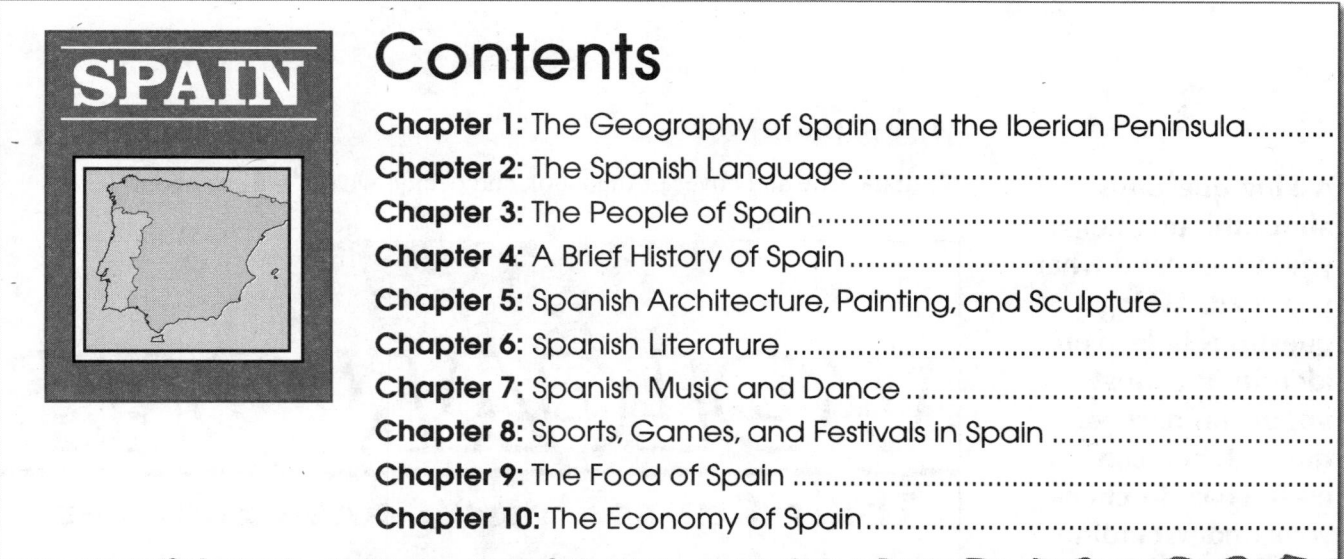

SPAIN

Contents

Chapter 1: The Geography of Spain and the Iberian Peninsula...........

Chapter 2: The Spanish Language ....

Chapter 3: The People of Spain ....

Chapter 4: A Brief History of Spain ....

Chapter 5: Spanish Architecture, Painting, and Sculpture ....

Chapter 6: Spanish Literature ....

Chapter 7: Spanish Music and Dance ....

Chapter 8: Sports, Games, and Festivals in Spain ....

Chapter 9: The Food of Spain ....

Chapter 10: The Economy of Spain...

Write your answers on separate paper.

1. What purpose might you have for reading Chapter 2?

2. What purpose might you have for reading Chapter 4?

3. If you were interested in examples of Moorish architecture in Spain, what method would you use for reading Chapter 5?

4. If you wanted to locate a recipe for the Spanish rice dish called paella, what method would you use for reading Chapter 9?

Use It

Read the chapter titles in this book on choosing a dog. If you were thinking of getting a dog, what would be important to know?

The Dog for You
Chapter 1: Things to Think About
Chapter 2: Family-Friendly Dogs
Chapter 3: Small or Large? Lively or Calm?
Chapter 4: Which Breeds Live Longest?
Chapter 5: The Costs of Keeping Different Breeds

Suppose you live in a small apartment. Or suppose you have small children. Which chapter(s) would be most important for you to read? Why might you want to read Chapter 1? Write your answers on separate paper.

Think of a major decision you have made. Did you read information on the subject? What sorts of things were important in making your decision?

Thinking as You Read

◆ *Questioning the Text; Monitoring Comprehension*

Asking questions about the text helps you understand what you read. Asking questions helps you identify the most important parts of the text. You can use a chart to check your understanding as you read.

This Is the Idea

Read the title and cover of this book and decide what it will be about.

From the title, subtitle, and picture, you can decide that the book is about volcanoes, what makes a volcano erupt, and what may result when a volcano erupts. You may know very little or a great deal about volcanoes, but in either case you are likely to have some questions.

Before you begin to read, you can focus your reading by thinking of questions to ask. For example, you might ask yourself, "Why do volcanoes erupt?" or "Where are active volcanoes located?"

You can also make a chart like the one below.

If you already know that lava flows from an erupting volcano, you would put that in the first column.

If you want to know what makes some volcanoes erupt so violently, you would write that in the second column.

You would use the third column to take notes as you read the book.

What I Know	What I Want to Know	What I Learned
Lava flows from an erupting volcano.	What makes some volcanoes erupt so violently, causing such destruction?	

Take a Closer Look

First, use the title and picture to decide what the article below will be about.

1. Now think about what you know about the topic. Write notes in the first column at the bottom of the page.

2. Think about what you want to know, asking yourself the questions listed on the right, and jot notes in the second column.

3. Now read the article, and as you read, make notes in the third column about what you learn.

Ask
- Who?
- What?
- When?
- Where?
- How?
- Why?

The Discovery of Coffee (Maybe)

People love a good story. When they can't find a true story to tell, they are more than willing to invent one. Consider the origin of coffee, for example.

Scientists believe that coffee plants originated in central Ethiopia and were first cultivated in ancient Arabia. However, mythmakers have stepped in to add details that research can't provide or confirm. One widely told story appears in many variations in many histories. It credits a herdsman in Ethiopia with the discovery of coffee. In some versions he herds goats, and in others he herds sheep. He's nearly always named Kaldi. Supposedly, Kaldi found his goats (or sheep) behaving in an unusually lively manner after eating berries from a certain bush. Kaldi tried some of the berries himself. He found that they made him feel especially wide awake and alert. Kaldi spread the story, and that eventually led to takeout coffee in cardboard containers— if you believe the story.

What I Know	What I Want to Know	What I Learned

Try It

Make a chart on separate paper. Fill in the chart before and as you read.

The Great Wall of China

The Great Wall was built as a protective barrier along the border of ancient China. Tradition says that Emperor Shi Huangdi first thought of building a Great Wall about 2,200 years ago. Archaeologists suggest that smaller walls had been built earlier, and the emperor's Great Wall project incorporated the older walls to save time and effort. Building continued for centuries.

By the late 1400s, most of the wall was in ruins. The Ming dynasty, fearing an invasion from the north, rebuilt it. Most of the Great Wall we see today was built at this time. Over the last 50 years, the Chinese government has restored parts of the wall.

Getty Images

The main part of the wall stretches 3,460 kilometers (2,150 miles). Other branches make the total length 6,400 kilometers (4,000 miles)—the world's longest artificial structure. It is no longer used for defense, but it draws tourists from around the world, as well as historians and archaeologists.

Use It

Read this passage from a book on body language. Keep in mind what you already know about the subject and what you would like to know.

On separate paper, make a chart like the one you used above. Fill it in before and as you read the passage.

Body language is more complicated than it might seem at first. For example, common wisdom says that crossing your arms is a sign of feeling threatened. The crossed arms form a barrier between you and the person you are talking to. This is true in some cases, but experts point out that there is another reason to cross your arms—it's comfortable!

Did you learn anything new about body language from the passage?

Choose a newspaper article that looks interesting. Read the headline and the first paragraph to see what it is about. What else do you hope the article will tell you? Read the article. Did it tell you what you wanted to know?

Reflecting After You Read

◆ *Summarizing and Paraphrasing*

This Is the Idea

As you read this history text, think about its main ideas and how you might summarize them. Think about how you might paraphrase what you read.

> As you read, pause now and then to summarize what you have read. Summarizing ideas helps you recall what you've read. Also, think of ways you could put what the writer says into your own words. Putting ideas in your own words helps you understand and recall them.

Marian Anderson

Marian Anderson's beautiful voice could move people to tears. Her talent was clear even when she was only a child. She first performed in public at age six in a church choir.

Still, she had problems early in her career. In the 1920s, the United States offered black artists few opportunities, so Anderson toured Europe, where she studied and sang. She became a major star there. By 1935, she was a top concert singer in the U.S. as well.

In 1939, a concert was planned for Constitution Hall in Washington, D.C. It was canceled after the owners of the hall—the Daughters of the American Revolution—learned that Anderson was black. This treatment angered Eleanor Roosevelt, the president's wife, and she resigned from the DAR in protest. The federal government then invited Anderson to sing on the steps of the Lincoln Memorial. She drew a record crowd of more than 75,000.

Anderson sang for 30 more years. In 1955, she became the first black soloist at New York's Metropolitan Opera. She performed before heads of state and won accolades internationally. She died in 1993, but her voice lives in her recordings.

Which sentence would you use to summarize the first paragraph?
  a. Marian Anderson certainly had a beautiful singing voice.
  b. Marian Anderson began her singing career at a young age.
Sentence b is the better summary, because it includes the main idea from the paragraph and leaves out the details.

Which sentence would you use to paraphrase the sentence in blue ink?
  a. Marian Anderson sang for world leaders and earned worldwide praise.
  b. Marian Anderson sang for heads of state and won international praise.
Sentence a is the better choice, because it uses different words to give the same meaning.

Take a Closer Look

Read this feature article and think about how you might summarize it. Think about how you might put it into other words.

**To summarize
a passage**

- Decide which parts
  are most important.
- Put the most
  important parts into
  a few words.
- Don't include details
  that are not very
  important.

**To paraphrase
a passage**

- Think about what the
  passage means.
- Look away from the
  text and imagine
  telling someone
  what it says.

The Iditarod

The Iditarod starts next week, and interest is running high. This sled-dog race runs from Anchorage to Nome in Alaska. The race began in 1973, and it takes place every year. Often called "The Last Great Race on Earth," the race covers about 1,100 miles. It is not merely a competition between sled teams, but also a battle between the teams and the elements.

History of the Race

The modern race recalls a race that sped medicine to Nome in 1925. The disease diphtheria threatened the lives of many children unless the serum arrived in time. It was January, and the only two available airplanes had been taken apart and stored for winter. So the serum was sent by train and dogsled. Twenty teams were used in relays to traverse hundreds of miles of frozen wilderness.

The last team covered 53 miles. The sled driver was named Gunnar Kaassen, and his lead dog was named Balto. At 5:30 a.m. on February 2, they arrived in Nome with the serum. The 20 sled teams had covered 674 miles in 127½ hours—just over five days. Balto was later honored by a statue in New York's Central Park.

Circle your answer.

1. Which is the better summary and paraphrase of the first paragraph?
   Hint: Make sure that all the important parts are included and that the
   ideas are expressed in other words.
   a. Next week's running of the annual 1,100-mile Iditarod sled-dog race in
      Alaska will pit sled teams against one another and the elements.
   b. The Iditarod race, which began in 1973 and is often called "The Last
      Great Race on Earth," starts next week, and interest is running high.

Write your answer.

2. Summarize and paraphrase the second paragraph, restating the most
   important ideas in as few words as you can.

   _____

   _____

   _____

   _____

Try It

As you read this gardening article, think about the main ideas. Think about how you would summarize them or paraphrase them.

Sharing Your Plants

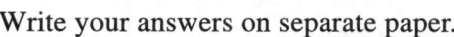

Many gardeners enjoy growing copies of their plants to share with friends. Different methods work with different plants. Almost all plants produce seeds that can be gathered and planted. However, the seeds from some plants produce offspring that are different from the original. Two other methods produce duplicates of the original.

Cuttings—After seeds, the most common way to make new plants is by making cuttings. The tip of a branch is encouraged to produce new roots. First, cut off several branch tips that are three to four inches long. Select healthy, growing stems that have leaves but no flowers. Place them in water or damp soil until new roots begin to sprout. Some plants can also be grown from leaf cuttings.

Many garden-supply stores offer rooting powders or liquids. Most treated cuttings will root faster than untreated ones. Furthermore, treated cuttings develop a larger root area, which gives plants a head start when they are transplanted.

Division—Another common way to make new plants is by root division. Simply dig up the plant and cut the root ball into two or three chunks. Cut from the crown down, and then replant each section.

Write your answers on separate paper.

1. Write a summary of the first paragraph of this article.

2. Choose a paragraph from this article and paraphrase it.

Use It

Read this petition, which is being taken door to door.

To the City Council:

We, the undersigned, feel that the city should change the speed limit on the 400 block of Oak Street from 30 miles per hour to 15 miles per hour. A lot of families with small children live on this block. We are afraid that a child will run out in the street when a car is coming. A car that is going 15 miles per hour has a much better chance of stopping in time than one going 30 miles per hour.

Isn't saving the life of a child worth the few extra seconds it will take to travel down this block?

On separate paper, summarize what the petition is asking for. If this were your block, would you sign the petition?

Has anyone ever asked you to sign a petition? What was the petition asking for? Did you sign it? Why or why not?

Using the Writer's Point

◆ *Using the Topic and Main Idea*

Many pieces of writing are about a single topic. The main idea is the main point that the writer makes about the topic. Sometimes the writer states the topic and main idea directly, but at other times you have to figure them out yourself. Keep the topic and main idea in mind as you read. Use them to check your understanding and to help you re-member what you have read.

This Is the Idea

As you read this section of a history text, look for the topic and main ideas, and think about the points that the writer makes.

Where East Met West and West Met East

The Silk Road was a group of overland trading routes that allowed the Chinese and Europeans to do business together. People began using these routes between 200 and 100 B.C. Traffic began to decline around A.D. 800, when safer sea routes were introduced. The last heavy use of the Silk Road was in the 13th and 14th centuries.

The Silk Road started at the eastern end of the Mediterranean and crossed through the Middle East and Central Asia, on into China.

The Traders: Europeans had a great desire for Chinese silk, porcelain, and spices. At that time, however, Chinese merchants generally did not venture beyond China's borders. So Chinese traders would transport their goods west, and then they exchanged them for wool, gold, jewels, or horses.

The merchants who now had the Chinese goods would carry them farther west, to other traders. Few people actually traveled the entire 5,000 miles of the Silk Road. Instead, each trader covered just a few hundred miles, always carrying goods farther eastward or westward.

Which of these could name the topic of the entire article?
  a. the Traders
  b. the Silk Road
Choice b is better because the whole passage discusses the Silk Road. Only the second section talks about the traders.

Which of these sentences tells the main idea of the first paragraph?
  a. People used the Silk Road until sea routes became popular.
  b. The Silk Road was a group of trading routes linking China and Europe.
Choice b is better because it includes all the important ideas in the paragraph.

Based on the writer's point in the last paragraph, which makes more sense?
  a. Trade along the Silk Road was a series of exchanges.
  b. Chinese goods were relatively inexpensive.
Choice a is better because it follows from the ideas in blue ink.

Take a Closer Look

Read this article and think about the topic, the main ideas, and the points that the writer makes.

Watch Out for Identity Theft

Identity theft is becoming increasingly common. A person or group uses someone's personal information to get credit, merchandise, or services. Victims may not even realize what has happened until they are denied credit.

Don't Be a Victim

Thieves use several strategies to gain access to your personal information, which includes name, address, income, date of birth, and bank account, credit card, and Social Security numbers. They may steal your wallet or go through your trash. They may call you and pretend to be your banker or accountant, saying that they need you to verify your Social Security, credit card, or bank account number. Once thieves have one of these numbers and your address, they order products or services, get credit cards, or order cell phones in your name.

You can't prevent identity theft, but you can make it less likely. Never give personal information over the phone to someone who called you. Don't carry your Social Security card with you. Leave it in a safe place, and don't write the number on your driver's license or checks. If you discard papers that contain personal information, shred or rip them first. Once a year, order a copy of your credit report from each of the three major credit bureaus: Equifax, Experian, and TransUnion. Check each report for suspicious transactions and mistakes. You may have to pay a small fee for each report, but in some cases you can get a free copy.

To figure out the topic, use

- titles and pictures
- headlines and headings
- repeated words on one topic

To figure out the main idea

- Look for general statements about the topic, especially in the first or last sentence of a paragraph.
- If the writer doesn't make a general statement, decide what the writer wants to say about the topic and turn it into a general statement yourself.

To use the writer's point

- Think about other ideas that the writer's point suggests.

Write your answers.

1. What is the topic of the article? *Hint:* Look for repeated words.

_____

2. What is the main idea of the first paragraph? *Hint:* Think about what the writer wants to say about the topic.

_____

3. What is the main idea of the last paragraph?

_____

Try It

As you read the following instructions, think about the topic and main ideas. Think also about the points that the writer makes.

GETTING A PASSPORT

U.S. citizens must have a valid passport to visit most other countries. Since it usually takes around six weeks to get a passport, apply well before you need it. You can apply at a passport agency and at many other government offices.

If you are over age 14, you must apply for your first passport in person. After that you can usually renew by mail. Both parents or guardians must consent to a passport for a child under age 14. If one adult applies for a child under 14, that person needs written consent from the other parent or proof of being the child's sole legal guardian.

To get a passport, you must prove that you're a U.S. citizen. You can offer proof by presenting an old passport or a certified birth certificate. If you were born in another country, you must show a consular report of birth abroad or naturalization papers.

You must also prove your identity. You can use an earlier passport, naturalization papers, a current driver's license, or a government or military ID card.

Finally, you need two identical small photos. These must be recent full-face photos that are two inches square and a good likeness. Casual snapshots won't be accepted.

Write your answers on separate paper.

1. Choose a paragraph from these instructions and write its main idea.

2. Think about the points that the writer makes. Based on these, why should someone hold onto an old passport even if it has expired?

Use It

Read this excerpt from a church bulletin.

Rummage Sale Planned—You Can Help!

There are lots of ways that you can help to make the St. Vincent's Church Annual Rummage Sale a success. You can donate things you don't want anymore (clean and in working order, please). You can volunteer to help set up the sale on Friday evening. You can staff the sale on Saturday. You can help with cleanup Saturday evening.

And you can buy, buy, buy!

What is the topic of the passage? How many different ways to help does it list? Write your answers on separate paper.

Look at a notice from a place of worship, a school, or some other organization in your community. Think about the main idea. What point is the writer making?

Using Important Details

◆ *Understanding the Significance of Details*

This Is the Idea

As you read this portion of a travel article, look for details that would be useful to someone who is planning to visit a city for the first time.

Tips for a First Visit

If you're planning to travel to a city you've never visited before, you can begin getting the most out of your trip before you even leave home. Get a good guidebook and use it to decide what features of the city are likely to interest you most.

If you are confused by new places and have a difficult time navigating unfamiliar streets, study a map of the city. Imagine yourself walking from one place to another. Make a copy of the map. Use a brightly colored marker to highlight sites you want to visit and the routes between them.

If you're going to bring children along, you'll want to know what attractions will interest them. One very good idea is to get a copy of the city's local magazine or Sunday newspaper. These publications usually list events that children will enjoy.

On your first day in the city, get an overview by going to the observation deck of its tallest building or by taking a brief but comprehensive bus tour before heading out on your own.

Details are the little things in a piece of writing. The most important details are useful to you. Some details help you understand the main idea. Others help you see why things happen or how things are alike or different. Still other details help you decide what makes sense or fill gaps in what the writer says. Details that do not help you are not as important, even if they are interesting.

The article offers detailed advice for travelers who are going to visit unfamiliar cities. Some details—the ones in blue ink—would be useful to anyone who was going to make such a trip. Others would be useful to particular groups of people, but not as useful to others.

The details in the second paragraph are directed to people who get lost easily in unfamiliar places. The advice in this paragraph would be very useful to those people. It wouldn't be useful to people who get around easily or who will have a friend in the city to guide them.

The details in the third paragraph are directed to people who will bring children with them when they travel. The details wouldn't be as useful to people visiting without children.

Take a Closer Look

As you read this newspaper article, think about why some details are more important than others.

As you read, ask these questions:

- Is this detail useful, or is it just interesting?
- What makes this detail useful?
- Will this detail help me understand the main idea?
- Will this detail help me decide what makes sense or fill in other details that seem to be missing?

Urban Wheels Opens

This new shop specializes in one type of transportation: motor scooters, which are the little siblings of the motorcycle. Urban Wheels is unique among businesses that sell motor vehicles in the city. Its owners design and build the scooters that they sell.

According to the owners, the Urban Wheels scooter has been designed to be a genuine alternative for urban transportation. It's not just for enthusiasts, but for people who will use them for everyday purposes.

For shopping, each scooter boasts a roomy trunk at the rear. Weighty purchases stored there are not likely to affect handling. The trunk is a lockable space out of sight and out of the elements. You access the space by raising the entire seat. It won't hold a week's groceries, but it will hold a large bag of groceries.

For some potential scooter riders, the disadvantages will be difficult to overcome. For one thing, a scooter offers no protection from the elements and no protection from other vehicles. However, they are fun to ride, use very little gas, pollute very little, and can be parked almost anywhere.

Write your answers.

1. What detail would be important to someone who was concerned about oil supplies and the environment?

   _____

   _____

2. What detail would be useful to someone who was thinking of buying a new vehicle for delivering takeout food in a city?

   _____

   _____

3. What detail would be important to someone worried about safety?

   _____

   _____

Try It

Why are some details more important than others in this employee notice?

Notice to Employees about Vacation Policies

How You Earn Time: Employees earn 1.53 hours of vacation time for every 40 hours worked.

How Time Adds Up: Vacation time is totaled at the end of each pay period. It is available at the start of the next pay period. Therefore, if you earn vacation time that brings you to a two-week total on a Friday, the two weeks of time will be available on the next Monday. The limit on total vacation time is four weeks. If you have four weeks of vacation time, no further hours will be added to your total until it is below four weeks.

How You May Use Time: Vacation time may be redeemed (taken as vacation absence) in units of one day (eight hours) up to the total amount available.

Vacation vs. Personal Time: Personal time is granted on a case-by-case basis for great personal need, such as caring for a child who is ill. It may not be added to vacation time.

Write your answers.

1. Someone is wondering whether a day or two of personal time could extend a vacation. What detail would be useful?

2. Someone wants to figure out how long it will take to earn a two-week vacation. What detail would be useful?

3. The writer doesn't say what the longest possible vacation is, but the details help you decide. What is the longest possible vacation?

Use It

Read this warning label from an over-the-counter medication. Notice the details.

WARNING!

△ Do not exceed maximum dosage.

△ Do not use this medicine if you have high blood pressure or diabetes.

△ If nervousness or dizziness occurs, stop using and speak to your doctor.

△ Do not take this medicine if you are on a sodium-restricted diet.

△ Do not give to children.

What detail would be most important for a parent? What about a diabetic? Why might someone be on a sodium-restricted diet?

Look at the medicines in your home. What warnings do they carry? Do any of these warnings apply to you or members of your household? How can you make sure the medicines aren't taken by someone who shouldn't use them?

Using Time Order

Articles about news, travel, and history include events. Directions and explanations include steps. The steps or events are usually mentioned in order, but sometimes they are out of order. If they are out of order, you can often figure out the correct order. Watch for dates, times, and key words.

This Is the Idea

As you read the following sports report, notice that the writer didn't put the events in order.

Hawks 3, Pythons 2

The first Python batter to face Hawks starter Hector Amado hit a home run yesterday afternoon, and the last Python batter to face him also hit a home run. In the innings between the home runs, the news was not so good, as the Pythons couldn't get more than one other hit and fell to the Hawks, 3-2, to drop to third place in the league.

Following the leadoff home run, the next two Pythons reached base, but then Amado, who is 9-1 in his career against the Pythons, settled down and struck out the side.

In the second inning, the Pythons fell behind after the Hawks' Kevin McLeod hit a two-run homer, and dropped two runs behind after the Hawks scored again in the third.

In the bottom of the ninth, the Pythons got their second home run, and the Hawks yanked Amado in favor of a reliever, who got the next two batters to ground out to end the game.

The account of the game sweeps quickly through the whole game in the first paragraph. The next three paragraphs give some details in order. It's as if we get the story of the game twice, once in broad outline and then in more detail. This arrangement of events is common in news stories. The writer gives a summary in the first paragraph for readers who want just a summary, then goes back and fills in the details for those who want them.

These four steps, which are listed out of order, have been numbered to show the correct order.

   2   The Hawks' Kevin McLeod hit a two-run homer.

   4   The Hawks' reliever got the next two batters to ground out.

   3   The Pythons fell two runs behind in the third inning.

   1   The first Python batter to face Hector Amado hit a home run.

Take a Closer Look

As you read the following history text, notice the order of events.

The Night the Great Ship Went Down

In one of the greatest sea disasters in history, the enormous ocean liner *Titanic* struck an iceberg 450 miles southeast of the Newfoundland coast just before midnight on April 14, 1912. It sank in less than 3 hours.

The iceberg that eventually sank the *Titanic* was spotted at 11:40. It was so close and the ship was moving so rapidly that the collision could not be averted. The *Titanic* struck the iceberg 37 seconds later.

The fatal events continued to unfold very quickly. In a mere 15 minutes, the mail room was flooded. The first lifeboat was lowered to the cold Atlantic a little more than an hour after the collision. Like most of the lifeboats that set to sea that night, it wasn't nearly filled to capacity.

When the *Titanic* had left Southampton, England, on its first voyage, bound for New York City, it was hailed with great fanfare as the greatest liner ever built. It was lauded as "unsinkable."

Just 2 hours and 40 minutes after striking the iceberg, the great ship and more than 1,500 of those aboard were gone.

Over the course of her last day afloat, other ships warned the *Titanic* seven times about icebergs in the area. But Captain Edward J. Smith saw no reason to slow down.

What shows the order?

- the order in the text
- dates and times
- key words, such as *after, as, as soon as, at last, before, begin, earlier, finally, later, next, now, started, then, until, wait, when,* and *while*

Write your answers.

1. What is one event that occurred before the iceberg was spotted and contributed to the *Titanic*'s sinking?

_____

_____

2. What reason do you think the writer had for putting the paragraph in blue ink where it is instead of at the beginning of the article?

_____

_____

Try It

Read the following news report and think about the events. Notice that the writer didn't put them in order.

Museum Director Retires

EASTERN CITY— At a press conference held today at the Eastern City Museum of Art, Claire Walker announced her retirement as director of the museum. This ends a 40-year reign as the museum's guiding hand.

Walker built one of the great collections of modern art at the museum. She ran fundraising parties and music events that increased the museum's endowment. She started the weekend family hours that attracted a new generation of young art lovers.

Walker's interest in art began in college. She organized an art club and began collecting the work of young artists. Many became lifelong friends.

©Heinz Hubler/
RubberBall Productions/PictureQuest

When Walker's professors recommended her for the position of museum director, she was, at 26, far younger than any other candidate. Even so, she impressed the board and won the position.

In recent years, Walker has suffered from heart disease, which last year forced her to assign day-to-day management tasks to her assistant.

Write your answers on separate paper.

1. How long ago did Claire Walker become director of the museum?

2. What events mentioned in the second paragraph happened *after* the events mentioned in the third paragraph?

3. What event mentioned in the first paragraph occurred *after* the event mentioned in the last paragraph?

Use It

Read this letter to a friend. Does it tell what happened in order?

Dear Dottie,

Guess what? I got the job!

I was so nervous when I went for the interview. I had bought a new blouse to wear, and I thought it looked very professional. But when I was getting ready, I found a stain right on the front! So I had to wear my old blouse instead. But maybe it brought me good luck, because I got the job!

Love,
Maggie

On separate paper, list the events in order. Why does the letter writer tell the last event first?

Look at letters you've written or received. Are events told in the order in which they happened? Why or why not?

Using Reasons

◆ *Understanding Cause and Effect*

This Is the Idea

As you read this sports report, look for causes and effects.

Denton Convinced Pythons Will Improve

The Pythons are off to their worst season start in recent memory, but Pythons manager Phil Denton is not worried. "We're a young team," Denton explains. "You have to expect that young players are going to make more mistakes than the more mature and experienced players, because they just don't have the knowledge and poise that experience brings. We've had far more than our share of bad luck, too, with injuries to our two best starting pitchers and our starting shortstop. But bad luck doesn't last forever, so I've got to believe that our luck will turn. Also, remember that it takes time for a team to jell, because the players have to learn to work together and anticipate one another's moves. I'm not worried, because I've seen teams get off to a slow start before, and some of them have gone on to have winning seasons, and even to win the pennants in their divisions."

Look for causes and effects when you read. To find a cause, ask, "Why did this happen?" To find an effect, ask, "What is the result of what happened?" Look for such clues as words, patterns, and pictures. Use causes and effects to check your understanding. You can also use them to help you summarize, predict outcomes, and make general statements about the text.

The manager of a baseball team is explaining why the team hasn't done well. He says that the causes are that they are inexperienced and have bad luck.

The manager predicts that the Pythons will improve for three reasons: because the players will learn to work together, because bad luck doesn't last forever, and because some teams have started poorly and have gone on to do well.

You can judge the manager's predictions by looking at cause-and-effect reasoning. It makes sense that if the players learn to work together, then the team will play better. On the other hand, bad luck in the present doesn't cause good luck in the future. The team's current bad luck will not affect its future luck.

There are two ways to understand the manager's third reason. He may mean that the Pythons *will* improve because other teams have. This reasoning would not make sense. There is no cause-and-effect relationship between the other teams and the Pythons. But he may mean that he knows that a team *can* improve because he has seen it happen. This statement would make more sense.

Take a Closer Look

As you read this history text, look for causes and effects.

Look for

- *because* or *since:* An effect happens because a cause happens.

- *if . . . then:* If a cause happens, then an effect happens.

- *so:* A cause happens, so an effect happens.

- *as a result:* An effect happens as a result of a cause.

Ask yourself

- What caused that? Why did it happen?

- What is the result of that?

Pierre-Charles L'Enfant, Visionary

Because he admired the goals of the American Revolution, Pierre-Charles L'Enfant left his native France at the age of 22 and went to America. He volunteered for the Continental Army. When the war was over, the new nation needed to establish a permanent seat of government. L'Enfant had been educated as an architect and engineer. In 1789, he wrote to President Washington, asking for the job of designing the capital.

L'Enfant was hired, and in 1791, he submitted his plan. It was a surprising one. The plan called for grand avenues far longer and wider than the young nation needed. They radiated from the center of the city and reached out into the sparsely settled countryside.

L'Enfant's vision of the future saw Washington, D.C., growing to be a great city and the capital of a large nation. L'Enfant was fired in 1792 as a result of many clashes with public officials. Even so, officials saw the merit of his vision, and they followed his plan for the city.

Write your answers.

1. What reason did Pierre-Charles L'Enfant have for leaving France?

   _____

2. Why was L'Enfant qualified to design the plan of the new capital?

   _____

3. How could you rewrite the sentences in blue ink, using the word *because?*

   _____

   _____

   _____

4. For what reason did L'Enfant design avenues that were "longer and wider than the young nation needed"?

   _____

   _____

   _____

Try It

As you read this parenting advice, look for causes and effects.

You *Can* Get Kids to Eat Fruits and Vegetables

Since children tend to prefer snacking to dining, turn vegetables into a snack. Cut carrots, celery, zucchini, peppers, and cucumbers into strips or chips and provide a dip, such as salsa, guacamole, or salad dressing.

When kids are hungry, they're likely to eat whatever is easiest to eat. If that is cookies and snack cakes, they'll eat those. If fresh fruit and fruit slices are the only thing available, they'll eat those.

Popular TV chefs know the importance of

presentation. They go to great lengths to make food look good on the plate, piling it high, decorating it, or arranging it in surprising ways. They know that appearance influences taste. They also know that it's fun to play with food, and that diners enjoy dismantling their creations as they eat them. Take a cue from them and create vegetables in stacks or encourage your child to play pick-up-sticks with string beans and a pair of chopsticks. You might even build a mashed-potato mountain with broccoli-floret trees.

Write your answers on separate paper.

1. Why, according to the author, will it help to turn vegetables into a snack?

2. Why, according to the author, is it a good idea to have fruit as the only snack available?

3. Why, according to the author, do chefs work to make food look good?

4. In your judgment, which of these ideas is most likely to succeed? Why?

Use It

Read this excerpt from a report on local schools. What reasons does the superintendent give for math score improvements?

Midland Valley Math Scores Rise

While reading scores on state tests remained steady for Midland Valley schools, math scores rose an average of 10 points over last year.

"We started special math review classes this year," said Midland Valley Superintendent Bill Black. "We also sent home a letter to parents asking them to make sure their kids got plenty of sleep the night before the test and had a good breakfast in the morning."

Which of the reasons given by the superintendent do you think had the most effect on test scores? What other reasons might explain the rise in scores?

Look for articles in the newspaper that give reasons for an event. Do you think the reasons explain the event? Might there be other reasons?

Using Groups

Classifying is putting things in groups. Writers usually have reasons for making groups. As you read, notice groups and think about the writer's reasons for making them. Notice how the things in a group are alike. Think about other things that might fit in the group. Think about how the groups help you understand the main idea or get the general sense of the writing.

This Is the Idea

Notice how contributions are grouped in this part of a business text.

The Arts Are Good Business

The arts improve the quality of life in a city. They also improve the economy of a city, both directly and indirectly.

Directly

The arts employ workers, pay taxes, and buy goods and services. Theaters, a symphony orchestra, museums, dance companies, art galleries, and auction houses all play the same role in a city's economy as any other business or industry. In addition to their operating expenses, they also make capital investments in new buildings and equipment. These contributions to the economy are easy to measure.

Indirectly

Arts institutions attract people in ways other businesses do not. These people tend to spend money on more than just admission to an arts event. They spend on meals, taxicabs, and baby sitters. The presence of an arts institution can anchor the economy of a neighborhood. It leads to the opening of restaurants and shops that cater to arts patrons before or after an event. In addition, many arts patrons come from outside the city. They bring income that most local businesses could not attract. These contributions are harder to measure.

The writer groups the ways that the arts contribute to a city's economy to make a point. The arts contribute directly and indirectly. They do what any other business would. They also help a city's economy in ways that most other businesses don't. Grouping allows the writer to show how the arts are like other businesses in a city and how they are different.

You might ask yourself whether these groups make sense. One way to decide would be to look at some other types of businesses. Is the writer correct that other businesses contribute to a city's economy directly but not indirectly? Is it true of a manufacturer? A bank? A university? A sports team?

Take a Closer Look

As you read these job requirements, notice how requirements are grouped.

As you read, ask yourself

- Why did the writer put things in groups?
- How are the groups related to the main idea?
- Can I make a general statement about the groups?

EMT and Firefighter Requirements

Q: What requirements will I have to meet to become an EMT or firefighter or get into the Fire Training Program?

A: Requirements vary somewhat, but in general to become an Emergency Medical Technician (EMT), you must complete a basic training program and pass an exam. You must be 18 years of age or older.

To earn a basic firefighter rating, you must be a high school graduate or have a General Educational Development (GED) certificate. You must complete an approved firefighter course. You must never have been convicted of a crime. You must be 18 years of age or older and in good physical condition.

The Fire Training Program provides advanced training to working firefighters. To apply to the program, you must first earn a basic firefighter rating. In addition, you must have at least an Associate of Arts (AA) degree or pass a Test of Adult Basic Education (TABE). You must have a report from a doctor stating that you are fit for heavy physical activity and pass a physical fitness test.

Write your answers.

1. Which of these opportunities would be open to someone who has not completed high school or the equivalent?

_____

2. Would a person who had been convicted of a crime be permitted to apply to the Fire Training Program?

_____

3. Would a person who is 17 years old be permitted to apply to the Fire Training Program?

_____

4. What requirements apply only to the Fire Training Program?

_____

_____

_____

5. In your judgment, why does the program have those requirements?

_____

Try It

As you read this health brochure, think about why types of care are grouped.

The Medicare Program

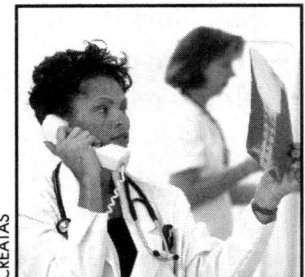

Medicare is the government's health insurance program for people over 65, those with permanent kidney failure, and certain people with disabilities. Medicare has two parts: Part A and Part B.

Part A (Hospital Insurance)

helps pay for care in hospitals, in some approved nursing homes, in approved hospices, and for some home health care. Most people get Part A automatically when they turn age 65 because they or their spouse paid Medicare taxes while they were working.

Part B (Medical Insurance)

helps pay for doctors' services, outpatient hospital care, and some other medical services that Part A does not cover. These include the services of physical and occupational therapists and some home health care. Enrolling in Part B is your choice. You will pay a monthly premium for it.

Write your answers on separate paper.

1. In general, what type of care does Part A cover?

2. In general, how are the kinds of care covered by Part B different from those covered by Part A?

3. From a budgeting point of view, how are Part A and Part B different?

4. Would Part A cover surgery performed in a doctor's office?

5. Why might a person choose to enroll in Part B?

Use It

This job evaluation form asks employees to rate themselves on each skill.

For each skill, circle O (outstanding), G (good), or N (needs improvement).

Basic Skills	Advanced Skills
O / G / N typing	O / G / N leading a committee
O / G / N filing	O / G / N organizing meetings
O / G / N taking phone messages	O / G / N training new employees
O / G / N sorting requests	O / G / N writing reports
O / G / N scheduling appointments	O / G / N doing research

Why do you think the skills are broken into two lists? What do the skills in the left-hand list have in common? Is there another way to break the skills into groups? Write your answers on separate paper.

Think of a job you have held. List the skills it required. Could they be listed in different ways, such as basic and advanced, or office and factory?

Using Like and Unlike

◆ *Understanding Comparison and Contrast*

This Is the Idea

As you read this consumer article, notice how the two types of shoes are alike and different.

A writer may compare things, pointing out ways that they are alike. A writer may contrast things, pointing out ways that they are different. When you read statements that compare or contrast, use what you find. Use it to get a general idea about the things that are compared or contrasted. You can also use it to make choices or to fill gaps in the writing.

Selecting a Sports Shoe

Any exercise shoes must fit properly to avoid injury to your feet. Both walking and running shoes should be large enough to fit comfortably over sports socks. The shoes should extend about a half inch beyond your longest toe. To get the most accurate fit, try shoes on in the afternoon or evening, because your feet are largest then. Since one foot is often larger than the other, try both the left and right shoes and make sure that they both give you enough space to wiggle your toes.

The motion of walking puts pressure on the heel and ball of the foot, so for a walking shoe you want good padding or cushioning in those areas. Look for a stiffer sole than a running shoe has, to assist your foot in shifting weight from heel to toe.

The sole of a running shoe, in contrast, should be more flexible, because runners want to be able to push off the ball of the foot with more forward thrust than walkers need. Cushioning is at least as important in a running shoe as in a walking shoe, but the desire for cushioning and the desire for light weight may conflict. For most runners, lightness wins out, but if you will be running on pavement, consider adding a bit of cushioning for greater safety and comfort.

The writer has organized the discussion into three basic parts, each with a paragraph of its own.

In the first paragraph, the writer points out buying concerns and shopping tips that are alike for both walking and running shoes.

The second paragraph focuses on walking shoes, pointing out qualities that make them different from running shoes.

The final paragraph is devoted to running shoes and the features and concerns that set them apart from walking shoes.

Take a Closer Look

Why are likenesses and differences important in this part of a history text?

Words often used to compare

- the words *also, both, like,* and *same*

Words often used to contrast

- words that end in *-er,* such as *taller*
- the words *but, however, in contrast, though, while,* and *unlike*

To use comparison and contrast, think about

- what you can say about the likenesses and differences in general
- why the likenesses and differences are important
- what they suggest that isn't said

The Erie Canal and the Panama Canal

Both the Erie Canal and the Panama Canal were major achievements, but for different reasons.

The Erie Canal was the earlier of the two, and it was much longer. It connects the Great Lakes with the Atlantic Ocean. The original canal was 363 miles long, and the entire system, with the feeders, is more than 1,000 miles. Like the Panama Canal, it uses a system of locks to make up for the rise and fall of the land.

The Erie Canal was begun on July 4, 1817. At that time, workers had only hand tools with which to construct the canal, and they had to battle weather, disease, and primitive working conditions. The project took more than 8 years to complete.

The building of the Panama Canal took close to 10 years. The Panama Canal connects two oceans, the Atlantic and Pacific. It is far shorter than the Erie Canal—about 51 miles—but a great deal deeper. Its minimum depth is 41 feet, while the average depth of the Erie Canal was just 4 feet when it was built.

In contrast to the workers on the Erie Canal, the workers in Panama had power equipment. Still, they faced other challenges, including landslides, malaria, and yellow fever.

Write your answers.

1. Why is the difference in challenges faced by the canal workers important?

   _____

   _____

2. Why is the difference in the depth important?

   _____

   _____

3. Given the similarities and differences between the canals, which seems the greater achievement to you? Why?

   _____

   _____

Try It

As you read these two classified ads for rentals, think about the likenesses and differences. Think about how you might use the information.

FOR RENT: 1-bedroom, 1-bath apartment within walking distance of downtown shops, museums, and theaters. Perfectly maintained and recently  painted, this cozy sun-splashed unit has a large living room with gas fireplace, a small but complete kitchen, and beige wall-to-wall carpeting throughout. The spacious bath has a washer and dryer, and the shower has both a seat and sturdy grab bars. A patio off the living room overlooks the harbor and provides a feeling of peace seldom found in a major city. The rent includes parking for one car, and a security person is at the door around the clock.

FOR RENT: 3-bedroom, 2-bath house on a fenced-in half-acre country lot. One master bedroom with walk-in closet, plus two smaller  bedrooms. One has built-in bunk beds, while the other has space for twin beds or a double. This home features a large eat-in kitchen, with a cooktop, oven, and double sink. A combined dining-and-living room would be a great spot for family gatherings at holiday time. Sliding doors lead from the kitchen to the backyard, where there's plenty of room for barbecues. An oversized two-car garage provides storage space for tools and garden equipment.

Write your answers on separate paper.

1. Which home would be a better choice for a family with children? Why?

2. Which home would be a better choice for a retired couple? Why?

Use It

Read these choices for ordering invitations. Think about the pluses and minuses of each.

Simon's Invitations

Our standard order is in lots of 50 and costs $45 per lot. This includes your choice of the artwork in our order books. Orders take three weeks to process.

Or you can custom order the exact number of invitations you need, with any artwork you provide. The base cost for this option is $1.50 per invitation, with added costs depending on the complexity of the artwork. Processing takes four weeks.

Which option would be more expensive for 50 invitations? Why might you choose the first option? The second? Write your answers on separate paper.

Look at a catalog that shows several types of one product. What are the differences between types? Which differences would be important to you?

Using Predictions

As you read, think about what is likely to happen as time passes, and then predict what will happen. Use your prediction to check your understanding and to plan what you should do. Use it to test what the writer says, including opinions, and to test general statements.

This Is the Idea

As you read this article, make a prediction after you complete each paragraph.

Lighter Than Air

At one time, experts assumed that the future of air travel would be in huge ships filled with hydrogen to make them lighter than air. It seemed unlikely that planes that were heavier than air would ever reach the size needed to carry really heavy payloads.

Time proved those assumptions wrong. Airplane technology progressed more quickly than the experts expected. The explosion of the hydrogen-filled airship *Hindenburg* made lighter-than-air travel seem too dangerous to pursue.

Some people are predicting a comeback for lighter-than-air craft. The primary reason is that large ships filled with helium can lift truly staggering payloads. These ships can carry loads farther and more cheaply than any airplane can. They wouldn't have the capacity of oceangoing ships, but they would be faster. Helium presents no danger of explosion.

Pausing after each paragraph to predict what will happen helps you make certain that you understand each paragraph. It also helps you decide what you think of the writer's ideas.

For example, after the first paragraph you might predict that if the experts were right, we would see many lighter-than-air ships today. Since we don't, the experts must have been wrong.

After the second paragraph, you might predict that if lighter-than-air travel seemed too dangerous, it would become unpopular. It did become unpopular, so you may guess that people felt it was dangerous.

After the third paragraph, you might make predictions about the future of lighter-than-air craft. You might predict that they could make a comeback—but only if they do something better than planes and if they are safe.

Take a Closer Look

As you read this advice about moving, predict what will happen if you follow it.

Moving without Breakage

Wrap and pad fragile things as thickly as you can. Newspaper is inexpensive padding, but the ink tends to smear and may stain fine china permanently. Use packing paper instead, which is newsprint without the ink. Plastic bubble wrap is an excellent protective packing material, but it's expensive; just as good, and completely free, are your towels and bed linens. Instead of packing these in cartons of their own, use them as wrapping and padding for your fragile dishes and glassware.

Pad the bottom of a box. Then wrap each item and place it in the box, adding padding between items to keep them from bumping one another. Be sure not to leave empty spaces that would allow the contents of a box to shift and collide. Pack fragile things in smaller cartons, like book cartons, rather than larger ones. Because you can't pack as much into a smaller carton, there will be less weight pressing down on the things at the bottom. The most delicate items of all should be double-boxed: wrap them thickly, put them into a small box and seal it, and then pack the entire box in another box with padding all around it.

These help you predict what will happen:

- a pattern of events
- the writer's point and conclusions
- causes and effects
- what you know and your own good guesses

You may want to

- stop something from happening
- make sure that something does happen
- check your understanding
- test an opinion
- check a general statement

Write your answers.

1. You can predict that if you pack fragile things in larger cartons . . .

_____

2. You can predict that if you wrap good dishes in newspaper . . .

_____

3. You can predict that if you use bubble wrap for all your packing . . .

_____

4. You can predict that if you wrap fragile things in towels . . .

_____

5. You can predict that fragile items in boxes with gaps . . .

_____

6. You can predict that fragile items that are double-boxed . . .

_____

Try It

After reading each paragraph of this history text, predict what will happen. Write your answers on separate paper.

A Tale of Antarctic Survival

A group of explorers led by Sir Ernest Shackleton set out in 1914 for Antarctica. They planned to traverse the frozen continent, passing over the South Pole. When their ship became trapped in ice, they had to abandon it. For months, the crew struggled across the ice until they reached relative safety on Elephant Island. But they knew they could not survive long there.

1. What do you predict probably happened next?

> Someone had to go for help. Shackleton and five others set out in a small boat. They sailed 17 days through the worst storm conditions, landing on South Georgia Island. If they could cross the mountains, they could get help. They didn't have proper equipment or maps, but they set out.

2. What do you predict probably happened next?

> In 36 hours, they reached the settlement across the mountains, but their troubles were far from over. They had to get back to their stranded companions. They failed three times on three different ships, but after months of trying they succeeded, and all hands were saved.

3. What would have made your predictions more accurate?

Use It

Read these instructions from the package of a microwave dinner.

Remove container from carton.
Cut film cover over meal to vent.
Cook on high for 4 minutes.
Let stand in microwave for 1–2 minutes before serving.
When cooking two packages, cook on high for 9 minutes.

Predict what will happen if you follow all the directions. What do you think will happen if you don't slit the film cover? What if you cook two packages for the same amount of time as one? Write your answers on separate paper.

Look at a frozen meal or other packaged food you have used. When you cooked this food, did you follow the directions exactly? Have you ever followed the directions, but the food didn't turn out as you expected? Why do you think that happened?

Using Clear Thinking

◆ *Applying Conclusions*

This Is the Idea

What can you conclude about the language of sailing from this history text?

Of Logs and Knots

In the early days of sailing ships, sailors needed a way to estimate their speed, but they had little technology to assist them. One simple way was to throw overboard something that would float and see how quickly the ship left it behind. Often, the something thrown overboard was a piece of wood, a "log." To make their estimates more precise, the sailors tied a rope—a "line"—to the log, and in the line they tied knots at regular intervals. As the ship raced on and the log floated behind, the line reeled out while one sailor counted the knots and another kept time with an hourglass. The captain, or someone designated by the captain, would write the results in a logbook—or log, for short—to record the ship's progress.

To this day, the speed of a ship is measured in knots, and a record of progress is still called a log.

Statements often work together. They may be linked by grouping, by cause and effect, or by likenesses and differences. When one statement makes sense, you may be able to conclude that another statement makes sense. Use what you conclude to check your understanding, to decide what you should do, or to judge an opinion.

The writer states that sailors tied knots in the line that held the log "to make their estimates more precise." From that statement, you can conclude that their estimates before that technique were not very precise. Note that you can reason your way backward to the cause. The sentence could have begun "Because their estimates were not precise enough."

To check your understanding after you have read the sentence in blue ink, you might ask yourself what you can conclude from what you have read so far. You might list what you know:

- Sailors needed a way to estimate their speed.
- One way was to see how quickly the ship left something behind it.
- They used a line with knots in it to make their estimates more precise.

From those statements, you can conclude that the sailors would let the line run out and count the knots as it did. You know that they wouldn't just hold the line, because then the log would not fall behind the ship. When you read on, you see that your conclusion was correct.

Take a Closer Look

From these tips on keeping warm, what can you conclude about staying cool?

Remember

- What is true for a group is true for each member of the group.

- Comparisons work in two directions: If X is bigger than Y, then Y is smaller than X.

- If something happens, there must be a reason, so you can reason from cause forward to effect or from effect backward to cause.

Staying Warm in Winter's Chill

If you are going to spend time outside on a frigid winter day, take precautions to ensure that you will be warm.

Stay active, because when you are, your body burns carbohydrates and fats to produce energy to keep going. One byproduct of that process is body heat, which your blood circulates, so the more you exert yourself the warmer you'll become.

Remain in the sun whenever you can and wear dark clothing so that you will absorb the sun's radiant energy and convert it to heat, as a cat does by lying in the sunshine.

Wear clothing that will retain your body heat. Traditional woolens, modern microfiber fabrics, or many layers of clothing will insulate you from the air around you, keep breezes out, and hold body heat in.

©Karl Weatherly/PhotoDisc/PictureQuest

Write your answers.

1. What can you conclude about adjusting your level of activity to stay cooler on a hot day?

   _____

2. What can you conclude about lying in the sunshine if you want to make yourself cooler?

   _____

3. What can you conclude about clothing and the air around you if you want to make yourself cooler?

   _____

4. What can you conclude about clothing and body heat if you want to make yourself cooler?

   _____

Try It

As you read this history text, draw conclusions from the statements in it.

The Camera Obscura

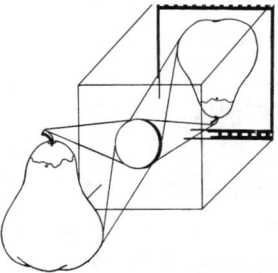

A popular entertainment in the 19th century involved entering a darkened room and watching moving images projected on a wall. That may sound like movies, but these images were not projected from film; they were images of the world outside, projected by sunlight.

This entertainment took place in a *camera obscura*, which means "dark room" in Latin. To make a camera obscura, you need a dark room with a window on the brightly lit outside world. Cover the window with dark, heavy paper or cardboard. The more completely you block light, the more successful the camera obscura will be. On the wall opposite the window, hang a large sheet of white cloth or paper. Then make a small hole in the window covering. If the light is bright outside, you should see an image on the opposite wall, upside down. Start with a pinhole, and then experiment with enlarging the hole very slightly until you get the best picture.

Write your answers on separate paper.

1. According to the article, where should the image appear?

2. What can you conclude about the quality of the image at night?

3. What can you conclude about the effect of stray light on the quality of the image?

4. What can you conclude about the size of the hole in the window covering and the quality of the image?

Use It

Read this catalog description of an adult education course.

Saving Lives

What if you were walking through the mall, when suddenly the person in front of you started choking or had a heart attack? Would you know what to do to save the person's life?

This course includes instruction in mouth-to-mouth resuscitation, cardiopulmonary resuscitation (CPR), and the Heimlich maneuver, along with other techniques that could save someone's life.

What can you conclude about CPR? About the Heimlich maneuver? Write your answers on separate paper.

Look at listings for adult education courses in your community. Do they describe exactly what will be taught, or do you have to form your own conclusions? What clues can help you?

Filling Gaps

◆ *Making Inferences*

Sometimes writers may omit details, causes, effects, or even the main idea. As you read, make inferences—good guesses—about what may be missing. Decide what missing information would fill any gaps the writer left.

This Is the Idea

Read this article about pets. What do the details suggest about causes, effects, and the writer's main idea?

Superstitious Pets

One golfer always wears green socks in a tournament. An actor always carries a silver dollar on opening night. A student wears a special good-luck bracelet whenever she takes an exam. These are examples of superstitious behavior. People take these actions because they believe, at least to some degree, that the actions will bring about a desired result. They associate the action and the result because once the two occurred at the same time. However, there was really no cause-effect relationship between them.

Animals kept as pets also show examples of superstitious behavior. I used to own a cat that, when it was hungry, would hop up onto a window seat and lick its paws for a while. Then it would turn and glare at me. It wasn't until the cat began audibly complaining that I understood. The cat thought that jumping up there was supposed to *make* me feed it.

What can you infer from the description of superstitious behavior in the first paragraph? The writer is suggesting that the golfer, the actor, and the student each had an experience that led to this behavior. The golfer won a tournament while wearing green socks. The actor carried a silver dollar on a successful opening night. The student was wearing the bracelet when she did well on an earlier exam.

What can you infer from the description of the behavior of the cat in the second paragraph? The writer is suggesting that an experience led to the cat's behavior. The writer thinks that the cat must have hopped onto the window seat once just before its owner went to the kitchen and opened a can of cat food. That coincidence led the cat to think that hopping onto the window seat *caused* the owner to feed it.

Take a Closer Look

As you read this advice on preparing for a speech, make inferences about the reason for each suggestion.

As you read, ask yourself

- Can I connect ideas to come up with new ones?
- Do my new ideas make sense, based on what I read?

If You Have to Give a Speech

Take a deep breath and calm down; you're going to make it through this, no matter how nervous you may be. Find out from the organizers how much time you are expected to fill, and tell the organizers that you want a lectern; insist on it. Write your speech out entirely, every word that you want to say, making sure that you haven't left anything out, and then cut it back so that you can say it all in the time allotted to you—certainly no more, but not too much less. Read the speech aloud, in its entirety, in a closed room to an audience of none. If it runs long, cut it and try it again, and keep cutting until your speech is the right length. Then practice delivering the speech without reading it, keeping it close at hand. When you reach a point when you feel that you have it all down, that you know your way through the speech and feel in command of it, stop rehearsing and take a break from it. When the time comes, take the entire written speech with you. Walk onto the stage and grip the lectern with both hands. Pat the written speech in your pocket to remind yourself that it's there, take a deep breath, thank the audience for its applause, and begin.

Write your answers.

1. How will it help you to know how much time you are expected to fill?

_____

2. Why is it important to keep the speech shorter than the allotted time?

_____

3. Why is it important to keep the written speech with you while you rehearse delivering it without reading it?

_____

4. Why is it important to stop rehearsing when you feel you are ready?

_____

5. Why is it important to make sure that there is a lectern?

_____

6. Why is it important to have the written speech with you when you give it?

_____

Try It

What do the details in this history text suggest about the electric car?

When the Electric Car Was (Briefly) King

In the early days of the automobile, the rivalry among power sources was keen, with the final winner far from certain. Steam engines, electric motors, and gasoline engines all vied for the crown. For a few years, electric cars were more advanced technically, performed better, and were more popular. In 1899, an electric car built by Camille Jenatzy of Belgium set the world's speed record. The streamlined car with a 100-horsepower motor reached a speed of just over 65 miles per hour.

Another auspicious event also seemed to favor electric cars. The first horseless taxis, which appeared in the 1890s, were powered by electric motors.

However, the favorable signs were wrong. In a few more years, the public had decided. New technology made the gas engine easier to operate and, by the late 1920s, almost no electric cars were left.

Write your answers on separate paper.

1. What can you infer about a keen rivalry?

2. What can you infer about Jenatzy's motor?

3. What can you infer about a speed of 65 miles per hour in 1899?

4. What can you infer about the meaning of *auspicious?*

5. What can you infer about public attitudes toward electric cars?

Use It

Read these instructions for using a loan firm's voice mail. Notice any gaps in the instructions.

"For your account balance, press 1."
"For the amount of late fees, press 2."
"To make a payment by phone, press 3."
"For a loan application, press 4."
"To speak to a representative, press 5."

What can you infer about questions you might want to ask that aren't included in the instructions? What should you do? Why do you think businesses use voice-mail systems instead of having someone answer the phone in person? Write your answers on separate paper.

Think of a time when you have made a call and ended up in a voice-mail system. Did the system give you the choice you needed? If not, what did you do?

Using Good Guesses

◆ *Applying Inferences*

This Is the Idea

Read this part of a nature article and think about the writer's point.

> # The Versatile Bamboo
>
>
>
> Although bamboo stalks look like tall, thin trees, the bamboo plant is actually more closely related to grasses. If you look at the stem of a bamboo plant, you will see that it consists of hollow tubular sections joined by thin solid sections.
>
> Despite amazing modern developments in synthetic materials, bamboo is still prized for fishing rods by enthusiasts. They like the springy way a bamboo rod whips through the air when they make a cast.
>
> Bamboo is also used for construction scaffolding throughout East and Southeast Asia. Many modern tall steel and glass buildings grow surrounded by scaffolding made with bamboo. The lengths of bamboo are lashed together with traditional methods that are ages old.

> **An inference is a good guess about something that the writer suggests but does not say. (See Lesson 13.) Use inferences to learn more about a topic, to decide whether the writer's statements make sense, and to decide what you might want to do.**

In the first paragraph, you learn that the stem of a bamboo plant is made of hollow sections. From that fact and what you know about hollow things, you can infer that a length of bamboo must be lighter than a solid log of the same size.

From the details in the second paragraph, you can infer that bamboo is flexible. It makes fishing rods that are springy and whip through the air.

The third paragraph describes a surprising use of bamboo. From the fact that workers use bamboo scaffolding to work on skyscrapers, you can infer that bamboo must be very strong.

Finally, from your three inferences, you can make a general statement about the qualities of bamboo that make it so versatile: "Bamboo is light, flexible, and very strong."

Take a Closer Look

As you read this consumer advice, think about what the writer suggests.

As you read, ask

- Do some ideas suggest other ideas?
- Can I use those new ideas to extend what the writer says?
- Can I use those ideas to test what the writer says?
- Can I use those ideas to decide what I should do?

LOW TECH = LOW COST

If you're thinking of buying a computer but find the prices of new computers daunting, think of the old story about how rapidly a car's value drops as soon as you drive it out of the showroom. That story is true, and then some, for a computer.

The reason is that many computer buyers want to be on the cutting edge of technology. They want the latest, lightest, fastest, and most powerful computer they can get, and that's not last year's computer. If you're willing to buy last year's technology or even something a couple of years old, you can get great buys. Decide what you need a computer to do, and find out how much speed, power, and memory that will require. Then buy a computer that meets your requirements, but don't buy more machine than you need.

Be sure to buy from a reputable dealer. Look in the yellow pages and find a firm that has been around for a while and treats you as if they hope to see you again. A good option is a firm that reconditions computers, making necessary repairs before reselling them and providing a warranty and service after you own the computer.

Write your answers.

1. What does the writer suggest about how rapidly a used computer's value drops?

_____

2. What does the writer suggest about how often cutting-edge buyers move to a newer computer?

_____

3. What does the writer suggest about the capacity of an older computer?

_____

4. What does the writer suggest about a business that treats you as if they hope to see you again?

_____

5. What does the writer suggest by recommending a company that provides a warranty and service?

_____

Try It

Read this opinion column. Think about the reasons for the writer's opinions.

A City Parks Endowment Fund?

The other day I received a fundraising letter from my alma mater. I always read these letters even though I make only one small gift each year. This time, the nature of the appeal caught my eye and it gave me an idea for our city parks. My college was asking me to give to the endowment fund. This, as you undoubtedly know, is the college's wealth, a large sum accumulated over the years and invested so that it will grow and produce income to meet the college's expenses. The endowment keeps the college from having to seek funding for every little thing every year. Instead, they raise funds for special projects, but the endowment keeps them going through thick and thin. If a college can establish an endowment, perhaps citizens can establish an endowment for a city's parks. If our parks had their own endowments, they wouldn't be in the state they've reached currently. If we begin now, we won't see results for years, possibly for decades, possibly even for generations. But if we begin now, we will be laying the foundation for the continued survival of these institutions.

Write your answers on separate paper.

1. What probably led the writer to write this column?

2. What can you infer about what a person's alma mater is?

3. What can you infer about the current condition of the parks?

4. If the writer wrote one last sentence suggesting what people should do, what do you infer it would be?

Use It

Read this shopping list. Make a guess about what project the writer of the list might be planning.

2 gallons of light blue interior paint
roller
paint tray
masking tape
stirrers
small paint brush

You probably guessed that the list writer is painting something. Can you guess whether it's a garage or a room? Why? Guess what the masking tape is for. Write your answers on separate paper.

Look at a shopping list or another list you made. Could someone else guess whether you were planning a particular project? If so, what clues might help?

Getting the Big Picture

◆ *Making Generalizations*

As you read, pause now and then to step back from the details. Think about the general meaning of the text. Try to make a general statement about the details.

This Is the Idea

As you read this advice for parents, notice the details and think of general statements about them.

Safe Equipment for Safe Cycling

Most children love bicycles because they provide independence. If you are buying a child's bike, choose it carefully and equip it well, since many biking accidents are the direct result of a bike that isn't right.

The rider should try bicycles to make sure that he or she can touch the ground while remaining seated. Don't be tempted to buy a big bike for a child to grow into. If riders can't balance themselves easily when they stop, their bikes are likely to tip over, possibly in traffic.

Young children should never ride at night, but older kids may have to. Be sure that drivers can see the bike and rider far enough ahead of time to avoid them. Bikes should be equipped with front and rear reflectors and headlights. They should also have reflective material on the wheels and pedals, and the rider should wear reflective clothing.

The most essential piece of equipment for child riders is a helmet.

In the second paragraph, the writer has included details about the importance of buying a bicycle that is the right size. A reader could make this statement about the details in that paragraph: "A bicycle that is too large can be unsafe." The details in blue ink support that statement.

In the next paragraph, the writer has included details about visibility. Based on these details, a reader could make this statement: "A bike and rider should be visible to drivers at night."

Since the advice contains many details that all deal with safety, a reader could make this general statement: "The right equipment can make bicycling safer for children."

Take a Closer Look

As you read the following language text, think about the general meaning.
Think about what general statement you could make about each section.

Ask yourself

- What is the general idea of this piece of writing?
- If the writer doesn't make a general statement, can I make one, based on the details?

The Development of an American Language

Like all languages, American English keeps growing and changing. Many influences have gone into making the English spoken today in the United States.

The earliest English speakers in America adopted many words, such as *moose* and *squash*, from Native American languages, as well as many place names, including *Manhattan, Chicago,* and *Minnesota.* American English also borrowed words from other languages. From Dutch came *cookie, boss,* and probably *Yankee.* Words loaned from French include *chowder, pumpkin,* and *prairie.* African languages contributed *cola, okra,* and probably *tote.*

When the American West was settled, the first cowboys came from Mexico and brought many Spanish words. The cowboys were called *vaqueros,* which comes from *vaca,* meaning "cow." Some English speakers pronounced this word "buckaroo." Vaqueros rode mustangs, pintos, or broncos, which they roped with lassos. *Mustang* is from the Spanish word for "stray," *pinto* from the word for "spotted," and *bronco* from the word for "wild." *Lasso* comes from the Spanish *lazo,* meaning "noose."

And the language continues to absorb new words. Immigrants during the 19th and 20th centuries helped add many words to the American vocabulary, especially words related to food: *delicatessen* (from German); *bagel* (from Yiddish); *ketchup* (from Chinese); and *pizza, spaghetti,* and *zucchini* (from Italian).

American English also lends its own homegrown terms to other languages. The word *OK,* first used in the 19th-century United States, is the best known. Today, speakers of many languages around the world use *OK* to mean "all right."

Write your answers.

1. What can you say in general about the effect of vaqueros on American English?

   _____

   _____

2. What can you say in general about the vocabulary of American English?

   _____

   _____

Try It

Look at the following chart showing the fat, calorie, and sodium content of some snack foods. What can you say in general about the different foods?

Typical Snack Foods	Fat (g)	Calories	Sodium (mg)
Apple, 1 medium, raw, with skin	trace	81	0
Apricot, 1 raw	trace	17	trace
Banana, 1 medium, raw	1	109	1
Cheeseburger, large, single patty, fast food	33	563	1,108
Chocolate chip cookies, 3 medium, homemade, with butter	14	234	164
Donut, cake-type, plain, 1 large	11	198	257
French fries, fried in vegetable oil, fast food, medium order	25	458	265
Potato chips, 3 oz., plain, salted	29	456	505
Strawberries, whole, 1 cup, raw	1	43	1
Taco, 1 large, fast food	32	568	1,233

Write your answers on separate paper.

1. In general, which type of food is lowest in fat and sodium?

2. What can you say in general about typical fast foods by comparing them with the other kinds of foods?

3. In general, which foods could people eat in quantity and still cut calories?

Use It

Read these rules posted at a public pool.

1. No running on pool deck.
2. Use diving boards only when area beneath is clear.
3. No dunking other swimmers.
4. Everyone must take a swimming test before swimming in deep end.
5. Children younger than 5 must be with an adult.
6. If you do not obey the lifeguards, you must leave.
7. No food or drink allowed on pool deck.
8. No street shoes on pool deck.

In general, what is the purpose of most of these rules? Do any of the rules have a different purpose? What? Write your answers on separate paper.

Think of public places where you have seen rules posted. Besides safety, what were some other reasons for the rules?

Checking the Big Picture

◆ *Testing Generalizations*

This Is the Idea

This opinion column discusses the facts shown in the graph. Do the writer's general statements fit the facts? Are they fair?

These figures show that the higher your income, the more likely you are to have a computer at home and to use a computer at home. That's not a surprise.

However, the higher your income, the more likely you are to have a computer at home **and not use it.** In households with incomes between $5,000 and $9,999, only about 4% of the people don't use computers

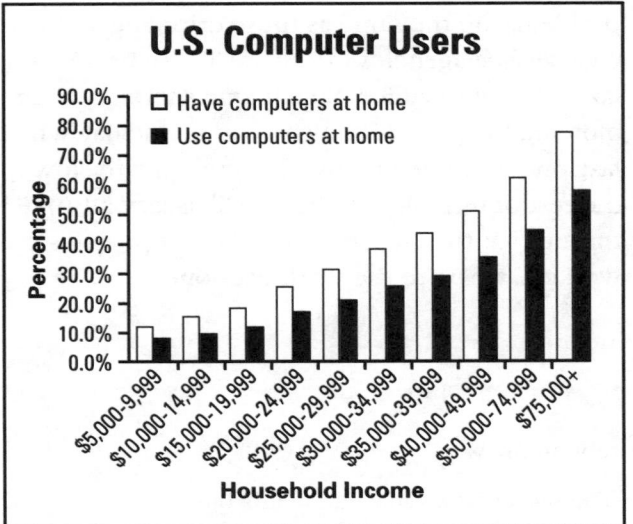

when they have them. The percentage of non-user computer owners goes up with each higher income group until it reaches almost 20%—1 in 5—of the people in households with incomes over $75,000.

This proves that low-income people who spend hard-earned money on a computer make good use of it. But wealthier people waste money on the latest gadget they don't need. This is clearly a case of "more money than brains."

As you read, pause now and then to make a general statement about the facts and ideas in the text. (See Lesson 15.) In addition, look for general statements that the writer makes. Compare the writer's general statements with your own. Decide whether they fit the facts.

The general statements are printed in blue ink. On the graph, the bars get taller as income goes up, showing that at higher income levels, people are more likely to have and use home computers. Also, the gap between the two bars—between people who have home computers and people who use them—gets wider. The first two general statements fit the facts shown in the graph.

The writer also says that low-income people make good use of a home computer and that wealthier people waste money on computers they don't need. And the writer implies that low-income people must be smarter than wealthier people. These statements *could* be true; they fit the facts, but they go too far. The graph doesn't show anything about how people use home computers, their reasons for buying computers, or how smart the people are.

Take a Closer Look

Think about the writer's general statements about workers in this letter.

Ask yourself

- Does the writer have enough information to make a general statement?
- Does the general statement fit the facts and cover all the facts without going too far?
- Is the statement fair?
- Does the statement match what I know or what another writer says?

To the Editor,

The city has just announced that revenues from recycling have declined. They blame competition from independent recyclers. As a result, the mayor is looking for ways to balance the sanitation budget and has proposed to cut back on recycling, make trash pickups less frequent, or charge extra for trash pickups on weekends.

I can tell you from experience that the sanitation department's problems are the same as those crippling all the city departments and civil service agencies in general. Those problems are waste and laziness. I worked for the city one summer when I was in college, mowing the grass in the city parks. One day when I was working too fast, one of the regular workers told me to slow down. "You're making the rest of us look bad," he said. This lazy attitude is rampant throughout the city agencies. If we kept a closer eye on the city's workers, we'd see the work get done.

Theodore Billings

Write your answers.

1. The writer bases his statements on one summer when he worked for the city. What is wrong with that as a basis for general statements?

   _____

2. The writer says that "all the city's departments and civil service agencies in general" are crippled by "waste and laziness." What is wrong with that general statement?

   _____

3. What would be a better general statement?

   _____

   _____

4. The writer says that "This lazy attitude is rampant throughout the city agencies." What is wrong with that general statement?

   _____

5. What would be a better general statement?

   _____

   _____

Try It

Think about the writer's general statements in this opinion column.

No Kids Allowed, Please

I think it is time to consider banning school groups from city museums. Last Thursday, I visited the Natural History Museum. It was overrun by school groups. The teachers and parents were too interested in chatting to control the children. Those children were completely bored by the exhibits. They spent their time running and shrieking and spilling drinks from the snack bar.

On Friday, I went to the City Museum of Art. The show of magazine cover paintings from the 1950s has been very popular and should interest children.

But the children at the museum were not looking at the art. They were running wild. They put real art lovers in danger of injury.

Bad behavior is taken for granted today among children. I suppose their parents do not bring them up properly. However, there is no reason to tolerate them in public places such as museums.

Write your answers on separate paper.

1. What is wrong with the general statement that the children "were completely bored by the exhibits"?

2. What would be a better general statement?

3. What is wrong with the general statement "Bad behavior is taken for granted today among school children"?

4. What would be a better general statement?

Use It

Read this note from a teacher. Are the predictions she makes justified by the facts she mentions?

Dear Mrs. Marcus,

I am having a problem with your son Robert. He never pays attention. When I am giving a lesson, he is always drawing or looking out the window.

I hope you will talk to Robert about this problem. He will never pass through high school or college if he doesn't change his ways. And his chances of holding a good job are small if he doesn't learn to pay attention.

Do you agree with the teacher's predictions? What are possible reasons for Robert's lack of attention? Write your answers on separate paper.

Think of teacher's notes or report cards that you or some member of your family has gotten. Did they ever include predictions? Do you think the predictions were fair? Did they come true?

Finding Facts and Opinions

◆ *Separating Fact from Opinion*

A fact is true and can be proved, but an opinion cannot be proved. An opinion is what someone feels or believes. Different people may have different opinions, but facts are true for everyone.

This Is the Idea

Which parts of this concert review are statements of fact?

Curtis Little in Concert

There was a time when Curtis Little was an exciting singer, with compelling material and excellent musicianship. His songs were about someone very much like Little himself, and the lyrics always made him seem like someone you would want as a friend. Those songs made him famous and brought him awards, fans, and millions of dollars.

Little's voice in Friday's City Park concert was strained and thin, without the conviction that he brought to the songs when they were new. Little now seems lost in the landscape that he once painted so colorfully in his lyrics.

He sang all his top-ten hits, but he seemed distracted, as if he were thinking of some other song the whole time. If his attitude toward his songs was bad, his attitude toward his audience was far worse, bordering on contempt. He left them asking, "With a friend like this, who needs enemies?"

The statements in blue ink are facts that you could prove.

You could investigate Curtis Little's career and find out whether he had become famous as a singer. You could use newspaper accounts or biographies of Little to find the facts. You could find out whether he had won any awards, and if so, how many and what they were. You might not be able to find out exactly how much money Little made, but you could probably find reliable estimates in business magazines.

The rest of the review consists of opinions, not facts.

The writer is a professional reviewer and knows a great deal about music and popular culture. And the purpose of a review is to present an expert opinion. However, all the statements in black ink are still opinions. Fans of Curtis Little and his music might disagree with them.

Even an expert opinion is still an opinion, not a fact.

Take a Closer Look

Look for statements of fact and opinions as you read this political endorsement.

Rosa-Maria Cruz for Mayor

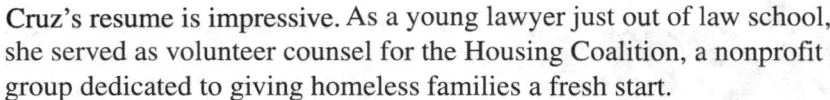

The *Evening Eagle* endorses Rosa-Maria Cruz for mayor of Eastern City.

Cruz's resume is impressive. As a young lawyer just out of law school, she served as volunteer counsel for the Housing Coalition, a nonprofit group dedicated to giving homeless families a fresh start.

She has served on the mayor's task force for reform of the city's schools. In that capacity, she did a superb job against intimidating odds, facing a school board famous for its contentiousness and resistance to change. For the past four years she has held elective office as deputy mayor.

For the past eight years, the city has enjoyed the enlightened leadership of Mayor Burke. The term-limit law does not permit Burke to run for the office again, but Cruz is a leader in the style of Burke. She has both the skill and the will to keep the city on its steady course.

To spot facts

- Look for statements that you could check somehow.

To spot opinions

- Look for such words as *should* or *must*.
- Look for words that name or describe emotions.
- Look for suggestions that something is good or bad.
- Remember that some types of writing— including editorials and reviews— normally express opinions.

Write your answers. *Hint:* Some sentences may contain opinions *and* facts.

1. Write three opinions from this endorsement; remember, an opinion tells what someone feels or believes.

   a. _____

   _____

   b. _____

   _____

   c. _____

   _____

2. Write three statements of fact from this endorsement; remember, a statement of fact can be checked somehow.

   a. _____

   _____

   b. _____

   _____

   c. _____

   _____

Try It

As you read this ad, look for opinions and statements of fact.

Lead the Good Life at
Gracious Gardens

©Ryan McVay/PhotoDisc/PictureQuest

Come visit Gracious Gardens today; you'll thank yourself for years to come.

At Gracious Gardens, you will discover a gracious style of urban living.

Discover the calm of our inner courtyard, where you will find a tranquil haven from the bustle of the city outside.

Gracious Gardens is conveniently located on two bus routes and the express subway line to downtown business and shopping.

Our staff is friendly, thoroughly trained, and fully committed to providing the highest possible level of service. We provide 24-hour security, and our repair crew is always on call should you ever have need of their skills.

In every apartment at Gracious Gardens, you will find the amenities that make everyday life a pleasure. We offer air conditioning in every apartment, individual storage lockers for every apartment, and basic cable television service, all at no additional charge.

Write your answers on separate paper.

1. Write three opinions from this ad.

2. Write three statements of fact from this ad.

Use It

Read this passage about dressing fashionably for little money. Notice which statements are facts, and which are opinions.

Most women are on a budget. They can't afford designer clothes. But you really don't need to shop at expensive stores to get that designer look.

All you need to do is buy top fashion magazines and copy the looks with clothing from discount stores. There's really no difference between a $2,000 designer skirt and a $15 skirt from a discount store, except the label.

And if having a designer label makes you feel more chic, copy it yourself, or make one up. Most people won't know the difference.

Which of the writer's statements are fact? Which are opinion? Is it sometimes difficult to tell the difference? Write your answers on separate paper.

Look at the photos in a fashion magazine, and read the descriptions that go with them. Are most of the statements fact or opinion?

Checking the Facts

◆ *Evaluating Statements of Fact*

This Is the Idea

As you read this section from a travel article, decide where you could check the statements of fact.

If you're not sure whether a statement of fact is correct, check it in a reliable source. You can check it in a dictionary, an encyclopedia, an atlas, or a world almanac.

The Walls of
LOS ANGELES

Los Angeles is a huge city, the second largest in the nation, with some wonderful public art, including the many public murals that appear throughout the city. They can be found inside public buildings as well as on outside walls. These murals are as varied and lively as the city that hosts them.

They are not only an art form, but also a means by which local people can communicate. One may show portraits of jazz artists, while another shows the results of an earthquake.

These murals differ from earlier ones, which often showed an idealized view of life in the United States. This vision often ignored the reality of life for non-European people. The modern murals are far more realistic. They show a variety of people, cultures, and levels of wealth.

The new street murals began to appear after the Civil Rights movement of the 1960s. Many minorities, including indigenous people, began using murals as a way to share their history, ideas, and lives. Some murals were created by named artists, including Elliott Pinkney and Jane Boyd. Other works were created by anonymous artists.

Some facts that you might want to check are printed in blue ink.

To check the statement about the size of Los Angeles, you could look in an atlas or almanac. An atlas would show a map of Los Angeles and some information about population. An almanac would give you the most recent population figures for Los Angeles as well as other U.S. cities.

To check the meaning of the word *indigenous,* you could look in a dictionary.

To learn more about the artists mentioned, you could look in an encyclopedia. You might look up the artists' names or the type of art.

Take a Closer Look

Read this history text and think about where you could check the facts.

These are reliable sources that you can use to check facts:

- A dictionary gives facts about words.
- An encyclopedia gives facts about general subjects.
- An atlas contains maps and gives facts about the countries of the world.
- A world almanac, such as the *World Almanac and Book of Facts,* gives facts about the events of the past year.

Note:

- The famous *Farmer's Almanac* isn't good for checking facts. A statement that sounds like a fact may really be a joke or a folktale.

THE *VASA*

The *Vasa* was a warship built in the early 1600s in Stockholm, Sweden. It carried 64 guns and was supposed to be one of the most fearsome warships afloat. It was also a highly decorated ship, with hundreds of figures carved out of various woods.

These mythological and historical figures were made to glorify the Swedish king and frighten his enemies.

However, when the ship set sail on August 10, 1628, disaster struck. The *Vasa* had sailed less than a mile when it was hit by a blast of wind; as spectators watched helplessly, the *Vasa* sank in Stockholm's harbor. Approximately a third of those on board died.

For more than three centuries, the ship lay undisturbed; then, in 1956, it was located and plans were made to salvage it. The decision was made to bring the ship up intact, if possible. Slowly, in 16 stages, the *Vasa* was raised, first to shallow water and finally to the surface.

The ship was like a time capsule from an earlier civilization. Partly because of the low salt content of the harbor water, many of the ship's contents were preserved. Divers found clothing, tools, ropes, table-ware, and food and drink.

Until the ship had surfaced, no one knew for sure why it sank. When scientists were able to examine the *Vasa,* they discovered that it was top-heavy. At the time, ship design was still primitive. Although tragic, the *Vasa* disaster gave modern people a glimpse into the past.

Write your answers.

1. What source could you check to find the location of Stockholm, Sweden? *Hint:* Think about which source gives facts about countries.

   _____

2. Where would you look to find the meaning of *salvage? Hint:* What source contains facts about words, including definitions?

   _____

3. What source could you check to learn more about the *Vasa? Hint:* Think about which source discusses general subjects.

   _____

Try It

Read this science text and think about where you could check the facts.

The Bald Eagle

Anyone who watches the bald eagle in flight will not forget the sight. This eagle is a magnificent bird whose wingspan can reach 8 feet. These enormous birds often soar on thermals, warm updrafts, with their wings outstretched.

©Alan and Sandy Carey/PhotoDisc/PictureQuest

During courtship, pairs may cartwheel through the air, whirling and tumbling.

Once an endangered species, the bald eagle has begun to recover and is now found over most of North America. Population estimates vary. Some scientists think there are 70,000 bald eagles in North America, including 35,000 in Alaska and 20,000 in British Columbia. Even so, the bald eagle is a "threatened" species that is in some danger.

Bald eagles are territorial and may stay in one area for years. They build large, strong nests and add to them over the years. Some nests have become as much as 9 feet across.

The birds that reach adulthood can live for decades. When adult eagles die sooner, it is often because of humans. Some are shot, while others die when they come into contact with power lines. Still others die from lead poisoning, after eating an animal that has been shot.

Write your answers on separate paper.

1. Where would you look to find the location of British Columbia?
2. Where would you look to find the meaning of *territorial?*
3. Where would you look to find more about Alaska?
4. Where would you look to find the most recent list of endangered species?

Use It

Read this ad for a diet program. How could you check whether some of these statements of fact are true?

WeighLess is a revolutionary new diet program that helps you lose weight quickly and keep it off for a lifetime! Our scientifically designed program will help you change those habits that led you to gain weight in the first place.

With WeighLess, you get delicious prepackaged foods that help you to lose 2–3 pounds a week. They are so good, some of our clients keep eating them even after they've reached their ideal weight! You will also meet with our certified weight loss counselors.

Some statements sound like facts but are too vague to be proved right or wrong. Find statements like this in the ad. Write your answers on separate paper.

Look at some ads in magazines or on TV. How could you check some of the statements?

Thinking about Opinions

An opinion is what someone feels or believes. When you judge an opinion, look for reasons and facts. Reasonable opinions are backed up by facts, research, and good reasons.

This Is the Idea

As you read this letter to the editor, look for facts and opinions.

Crackpot Educational Theories

Last week, the school board released the new budget. To no one's surprise, there were deep cuts in several programs.

While many programs have been trimmed, the music program has remained uncut. Keeping music and cutting industrial arts is a serious mistake. After all, industrial arts teaches practical skills that every student will need some day. Music adds pleasure to our lives, but most people could live without it.

Our school board seems to have fallen for a crackpot theory called "the Mozart effect." Some magazine had an article awhile back saying that listening to Mozart made people smarter, and now everyone has decided that hearing classical music can make geniuses out of children. Some magazine promotes music, and suddenly our tax dollars go to music instead of more important subjects. As taxpayers, we should object to this waste of money; as parents, we should worry about our children, who are far more likely to need to know how to build a fence than how to compose a song.

Most of the first paragraph is factual. By reading the school budget you could check whether programs had been cut, and which ones.

The next paragraph states an opinion and supports it with facts and reasons. The writer thinks that industrial arts is more important than music because it is more useful. In general, you can see that the writer favors industrial arts over music.

The next paragraph contains more opinions. The writer offers reasons, but they are not convincing reasons. The reference to "some magazine" cannot be checked. The paragraph also includes a general statement that cannot be supported by facts. It is unlikely that "everyone" believes that "music can make geniuses out of children."

In an attempt to persuade readers, the writer also uses such negative words as *crackpot* and *waste,* which are themselves statements of opinion.

Take a Closer Look

Read this column, and think about the writer's opinion.

OUR SCHOOL'S MUSIC PROGRAM

Music serves many functions. It gives students a means of expression that does not depend on words, which allows students who have poor language skills to communicate. Through music, they learn to express themselves and also learn about the creative process.

Students who study music, rather than merely listening to it, show real improvement in several areas. In one study in the Downey, California, Unified School District, first-grade students who had studied music for a year scored better in reading than other classmates. In another study that dealt with older students, those who studied music and arts for four years scored higher on college board tests. Their combined math and language scores were 52 points higher than the scores of those who had studied for just one year.

Scientists now think that studying music may help to develop parts of the brain. In addition, it seems to help students in other ways as well. They learn discipline and the importance of practice, and they strengthen problem-solving and listening skills.

Since we added our new music program, our dropout rate has fallen sharply. This may be because music reaches students who have had little school success before, or perhaps students just enjoy school more. Whatever the reason, it shows that music has an essential role in education.

Ask yourself these questions when you read opinions:

- Does the writer support the opinions with facts, research, and good reasons?
- Could I have predicted the opinion from the facts and reasons that were given?

Write your answers.

1. What is the writer's opinion about music in school? *Hint:* The writer states it *after* offering reasons and facts as support.

   _____

   _____

2. What are three facts that the writer gives to support this opinion?
   Hint: Remember that a statement of fact can be checked.

   _____

   _____

   _____

Try It

Use the facts and reasons in this part of a letter to predict the writer's opinion.

To the Editor,

Last week I witnessed a miracle. I watched the sixth-grade musical production of *Top Dog.* Like many other school plays, it had moments of unintended humor, with kids who forgot their lines or the words to a song, and sound effects that sounded at odd times.

The miracle was that my son memorized  two songs and sang them in front of an audience. Those of you who know Jared recognize what an achievement that is. He is usually quite shy in front of strangers, yet last Friday and Saturday he stood on a stage and belted out two songs.

One reason, I think, is that every classmate was involved. This was a group effort, and Mr. Ramoz, the drama teacher, surely made that clear. Credit must also go to Ms. Woodward, the music teacher, because she coaxed some wonderful performances out of the cast.

Knowing that many kids enjoy popular music, she encouraged them to mimic the moves and sounds of some popular singers. The performers got so involved in the fun that they forgot to be self-conscious, and the enthusiasm of other students helped performers, like my son, forget their shyness. The audience's applause will certainly encourage them to perform again.

Write your answers on separate paper.

1. What opinion about music in the schools do you predict this writer will state at the end of the letter?

2. What are two reasons or facts that the writer offers that would support that opinion?

Use It

Read this statement about thumb-sucking. Is the writer's opinion supported by facts?

If your toddler sucks his thumb, will it lead to braces later on? Yes, absolutely! My daughter Emily sucked her thumb from the day she was born until she got braces at age 8. My son Danny, on the other hand, never sucked his thumb and never needed braces.

Do yourself a favor. If you see your child sucking his thumb, do whatever you have to do to get him to stop. It'll save you lots of money down the road.

To support his case, the writer tells what happened in her own family. Does this prove her case? Why or why not? Write your answer on separate paper.

Many people have strong opinions on child-rearing matters, such as toilet training and the use of pacifiers. Look up one of these issues in a child-care book. Does the writer use facts to back up an opinion?

Thinking about the Author

◆ *Evaluating an Author's Viewpoint, Purpose, and Bias*

This Is the Idea

As you read this letter, think about the writer's purposes for writing it.

To the Editor,

I recently visited my daughter's school, and there in the cafeteria I saw a row of vending machines. These machines sell the following items: potato chips, corn chips, candy bars, cookies, snack cakes, and carbonated soft drinks. It is difficult for me to express my outrage at seeing these machines there in the cafeteria of a public elementary school.

These vending machines teach a very bad lesson, the lesson that the school thinks that it is perfectly all right for a growing child to substitute a lunch of cake, candy, and cola for the balanced lunch the cafeteria serves.

The school system should not be teaching such a lesson.

Clearly, profit is the motive behind the introduction of these machines—profit at the expense of our children. Our children must not be pawns in a marketing campaign.

A Concerned Parent

As you read, think about the writer. Think about the opinions that the writer seems to hold. Think about why the writer wrote what you are reading. What purpose underlies it? Decide what the writer wants you to think or do. Think about whether the writer might gain something from convincing you to agree or persuading you to do something.

What views and opinions does the writer of the letter seem to hold? It would be fair to say that the writer is strongly opposed to having commercial vending machines in a public school. The writer is also clearly opposed to making snack food of the "cake, candy, and cola" type available to children in a public school.

What did the writer want to accomplish by writing this? The writer seems to have two goals. One is to persuade readers to agree with the writer's ideas and opinions. The other is to persuade readers to object to the vending machines in the schools, perhaps by writing to the school board.

What does the writer want the reader to think or do after reading this? The writer wants the reader to agree that vending machines and snack foods are inappropriate in a public school.

Ultimately, the writer wants to see the snack vending machines removed from the schools.

Take a Closer Look

As you read this letter to parents, think about the writer's purposes.

**As you read,
ask yourself**

- What views and opinions does the writer seem to hold?
- What purpose did the writer have for writing this?
- What does the writer want me to think or do after I have read it?
- Will the writer gain anything from changing my mind or persuading me to do something?

To Parents:

Recently a parent of an elementary school pupil has written to the board objecting to the vending machines that have been installed in the cafeterias of the city's schools.

We are writing to assure parents that our schools are committed to providing students with nutritionally balanced meals through our school lunch and school breakfast programs. The vending machines in the elementary school cafeterias are not intended to replace those meals, but merely to supplement them.

We all know that elementary school children get hungry at times and need a snack to keep them going. How many of us, as adults, find ourselves slowing down a bit in the middle of the afternoon and reach for a candy bar or cup of coffee? Just as we do, children sometimes need the boost from a snack to keep them at their learning peak.

The fees paid by the vending firm go into the general budget, helping to offset recent cutbacks and ensure that we can continue to provide a high-quality education for all pupils.

The School Board

Write your answers.

1. What are two views or opinions that the writer seems to hold?

   _____

   _____

2. What purpose do you think the writer had for writing this?

   _____

   _____

3. What does the writer want readers to think or do after reading this?

   _____

   _____

4. Does the writer have anything to gain from persuading people to agree with the sentences in blue ink?

   _____

   _____

Try It

As you read this editorial, think about the writer's purposes.

Reading, Writing, and Vending Machines

The Board of Education has, in its wisdom, allowed the installation of vending machines in elementary school cafeterias. These machines are stocked with the types of snack that are usually called "junk"; they are high in calories and low in nutritional value. They lure hungry youngsters with sugar, salt, and caffeine.

A growing group of parents objects to these vending machines and the snacks that they purvey. So do we.

The school board is being less than honest when it claims that these vending machines are not a substitute for cafeteria meals. It seems very unlikely that the board intended the snack foods as a substitute for the cafeteria meals, but it also seems very unlikely that the board doesn't realize that some pupils will think that they make a very good substitute.

We think that the board should be honest with parents, admit that the vending machines were a bad idea, and have them removed.

Write your answers on separate paper.

1. What are two views or opinions that the writer seems to hold?

2. What purpose do you think the writer had for writing this?

3. What does the writer want readers to think or do after reading this?

Use It

Read this flyer posted outside a hospital. Think about why the writer wrote it.

Montcalm Hospital Aides—Are You Tired?

✓ Are you tired of doing more work for less money?
✓ Are you tired of being treated with no respect?
✓ Are you tired of poor patient care being blamed on you instead of on understaffing?

Come to a meeting of the
National Association of Hospital Workers
Friday, 6 p.m., Mike's Restaurant

What is the purpose of this flyer? Who do you think would write this, a staff member or someone from outside?

Have you worked at a place where some workers wanted to form a union? Did you see flyers like this one? How did the management tell its side?

ReadingWise Strategies

Strategy	How to use the strategy
Using context clues	When you find a word you don't know, look for definitions, synonyms, or other context clues that can help you figure out the meaning.
Predicting content; setting a purpose and method	Before you start to read, skim the text to get an idea of what it's about. Look for titles, headings, and key words. To understand something in depth, read slowly. To find certain facts or get a general idea, read quickly. To help yourself remember, take notes.
Questioning the text; monitoring comprehension	Asking questions about the text helps you understand what you read. As you read, ask yourself, "Who? What? When? Where? How? Why?" You can use a chart to check your understanding as you read.
Summarizing and paraphrasing	To summarize a passage, decide which parts are most important and put them into a few words. Don't include details that are not very important. To paraphrase a passage, think about what the passage means, look away from the text, and imagine telling someone what it says.
Using the topic and main idea	To figure out the topic, use titles, pictures, headlines and headings, and repeated words on one topic. To figure out the main idea, look for general statements about the topic, especially in the first or last sentence of a paragraph. If the writer doesn't make a general statement, decide what the writer's main point is and turn it into a general statement.
Understanding the significance of details	The most important details are useful. As you read, ask yourself, "Is this detail useful, or is it just interesting? What makes this detail useful? Will it help me understand the main idea, decide what makes sense, or fill in missing details?"
Understanding sequence	If steps or events are out of order, you can often figure out the correct order. Watch for dates, times, and key words that relate to time.
Understanding cause and effect	To understand cause and effect, look for clues such as words, patterns, and pictures. To find a cause, ask, "Why did this happen? What caused it?" To find an effect, ask, "What is the result of what happened?"
Understanding classification	As you read, notice groups. Ask yourself, "Why did the writer put things in groups? How are the groups related to the main idea? Can I make a general statement about the groups?"

Understanding comparison and contrast	To use comparisons and contrast, think about • what you can say about the likenesses and differences in general • why the likenesses and differences are important • what the likenesses and differences suggest that isn't said
Applying predictions of outcome	As you read, predict what will happen next. Use your predictions to stop something from happening, to make sure that something does happen, to check your understanding, or to test an opinion or general statement.
Applying conclusions	When one statement makes sense, you may be able to conclude that another statement makes sense. Remember • What is true for a group is true for each member of the group. • Comparisons work both ways: If X is bigger than Y, then Y is smaller than X. • If something happens, there must be a reason, so you can reason from cause forward to effect or from effect backward to cause.
Making inferences	As you read, make inferences about any gaps the writer left. Ask yourself, "Can I connect ideas to come up with new ones? Do my new ideas make sense?"
Applying inferences	To apply your inferences, ask yourself, "Can I use my inferences to extend what the writer says? To test what the writer says? To decide what I should do?"
Making generalizations	As you read, pause now and then. Try to make a general statement about the details.
Testing generalizations	Think about general statements the writer makes. Ask yourself, "Does the writer have enough information to make a general statement? Does the statement fit the facts and cover all the facts without going too far? Is the statement fair? Does the statement match what I know or what another writer says?"
Separating fact from opinion	To spot facts, look for statements that you could check somehow. To spot opinions • Look for words such as *should* and *must*. • Look for words that name or describe emotions. • Look for suggestions that something is good or bad. • Remember that some types of writing—including editorials and reviews—normally express opinions.
Evaluating statements of fact	If you're not sure whether a statement of fact is correct, you can check it in a dictionary, encyclopedia, atlas, world almanac, or other reliable source.
Evaluating opinions	When you judge an opinion, look for reasons and facts. Ask yourself, "Does the writer support the opinions with facts, research, and good reasons?"
Evaluating an author's viewpoint, purpose, and bias	As you read, ask yourself, "What views and opinions does the writer seem to hold? What purpose did the writer have for writing this? What does the writer want me to think or do after I have read this? Will the writer gain anything from changing my mind or persuading me to do something?"

Answer Key

Lesson 1

Take a Closer Look

1. a middle ground between extremes

2. a large company that grants a franchise to a small-business operator

3. a small-business operator who enters into a franchise agreement with a large company

4. an agreement that works both ways, with benefits for both parties

5. set, impose

6. prevented, forbidden

Try It

1. suspicious, unbelieving

2. say, claim

3. small, tiny

4. enough, adequate

5. unusual, not typical

Use It

Answers will vary.

Lesson 2

Take a Closer Look

1. Answers will vary.

2. to find out where you can vote

3. "A Long, Hard Campaign"

4. Answers will vary.

Try It

Answers may vary. Here are some examples:

1. to find out how the language spoken in Spain compares with the Spanish spoken in North America

2. to get an overview of Spanish history

3. read slowly and carefully the parts of the chapter that are about architecture

4. skim quickly until you find information about paella; then read slowly and carefully

Use It

Answers will vary.

Lesson 3

Take a Closer Look

1. Answers will vary but should be put under "What I Know."

2. Answers will vary but should be put under "What I Want to Know."

3. Answers will vary but should be put under "What I Learned."

Try It

Answers will vary.

Use It

Answers will vary.

Lesson 4

Take a Closer Look

1. a

2. Answers will vary.

Try It

Answers will vary.

Use It

Answers will vary.

Lesson 5

Take a Closer Look

1. what identity theft is and how to prevent it

2. Identity theft is secretly using someone's personal information to get credit or make purchases.

3. You can take steps to make identity theft less likely.

Try It

1. Answers will vary. These are main ideas for each paragraph in order:

    Citizens traveling outside the U.S. must have passports, which they can apply for at many places.

    Adults and children over 14 must apply for a passport in person; for children under 14, both parents must consent.

    You must prove that you're a citizen.

    You must prove your identity.

    You must provide two identical pictures.

2. An old passport can be used to get a new one. It proves both citizenship and identity.

Use It

Topic: How to help with the St. Vincent's Church Annual Rummage Sale

Ways to help: donate things, set up on Friday, staff the sale on Saturday, help with cleanup Saturday evening, and buy, buy, buy.

Lesson 6

Take a Closer Look

1. Scooters use very little gas and pollute very little.

2. Each scooter boasts a roomy trunk in the rear.

3. A scooter offers no protection from the elements and no protection from other vehicles.

Try It

1. Personal time may not be added to vacation time.

2. Employees earn 1.53 hours of vacation time for every 40 hours worked.

3. Four weeks. The notice says that four weeks is the most vacation time that an employee can have available. It also says that employees can take vacation time up to the total amount available. Therefore, four weeks is the most vacation time an employee can take at one time.

Use It

Answers may vary. Here are some examples:

For a parent: Do not give this medicine to children.

For a diabetic: Do not use this medicine if you have diabetes.

Lesson 7

Take a Closer Look

1. Other ships sent iceberg warnings, but the captain saw no reason to slow down.

2. Putting it there increases its dramatic impact and the impact of the paragraph that immediately follows it.

Try It

1. 40 years ago

2. All the events in the second paragraph happened after the events in the third paragraph.

3. At a press conference held today at the Eastern City Museum of Art, Claire Walker announced her retirement as director of the museum.

Use It

Answers may vary. Here is one possible list:

Maggie bought a new blouse.

Maggie found a stain on the new blouse.

Maggie wore her old blouse.

Maggie went to the interview.

Maggie got the job.

Lesson 8

Take a Closer Look

1. He admired the goals of the American Revolution.

2. He had been educated as an architect and engineer.

3. L'Enfant's plan was surprising because it called for grand avenues far longer and wider than the young nation needed.

4. because he foresaw that Washington, D.C., would one day be the capital of a large nation

Try It

1. because children prefer snacking to dining

2. because hungry kids will eat whatever is easiest to eat

3. because they know that appearance influences taste

4. Answers will vary.

Use It

Answers will vary.

Lesson 9

Take a Closer Look

1. EMT

2. no

3. no

4. have at least an Associate of Arts (AA) degree or pass a Test of Adult Basic Education (TABE)

   have a report from a doctor stating that you are fit for heavy physical activity

   pass a physical fitness test

5. Answers will vary.

Try It

1. care in a hospital or other institution

2. They are for services outside a hospital or other institution.

3. Part A is free for most people; there is a monthly premium for Part B.

4. no

5. to get coverage for services not covered by Part A

Use It

Answers will vary.

Lesson 10

Take a Closer Look

1. It shows that work on both canals was difficult, even though workers faced different challenges.

2. It shows that large oceangoing ships could pass through the Panama Canal but not the Erie Canal.

3. Answers will vary.

Try It

Answers may vary. Here are some examples:

1. the house, because it offers enough space for children and a kitchen large enough to cook for a family

2. the apartment, because it is the right size for just two people

Use It

A custom order would be more expensive for 50 invitations. Reasons will vary.

Lesson 11

Take a Closer Look

1. the things at the bottom are more likely to break

2. they may get smeared with ink

3. things will be well protected, but you will spend a lot of money

4. they will be well protected and you will save money

5. are more likely to break

6. will arrive safely

Try It

Answers may vary. Here are some examples:

1. Someone tried to go for help.

2. The title of the reading mentions "survival," so they probably succeeded.

3. more information

Use It

Answers will vary.

Lesson 12

Take a Closer Look

1. Be as inactive as possible to stay cooler.

2. It's a bad idea.

3. You should wear clothing that lets the air reach you and lets breezes in.

4. You should wear clothing that lets your body heat escape.

Try It

1. on the wall opposite the window

2. It will be poor.

3. It will lower the quality.

4. Even small changes will affect the quality of the image.

Use It

Answers may vary. Here is an example:

CPR and the Heimlich maneuver could save some-one's life.

Lesson 13

Take a Closer Look

Answers may vary. Here are some examples:

1. You can make the speech the right length.

2. because people don't like speeches that run long

3. so that if you forget something, you can look it up

4. so your speech won't get "stale"

5. so you have something to hold onto if you're nervous

6. so that you know if you forget something, you can read it from the written speech

Try It

1. It is a fierce competition.

2. It was advanced for the time.

3. It was very fast for the time.

4. It means "favorable."

5. They changed dramatically in a few years, from positive to negative.

Use It

Answers will vary.

Lesson 14

Take a Closer Look

Answers may vary. Here are some examples:

1. It drops even faster than a used car's value.

2. They move on often.

3. It can be enough to meet many people's needs.

4. They are more likely to stay in business.

5. You may have some problems that need service or repair.

Try It

1. Answers will vary.

2. It is the college the person attended.

3. The parks are in bad condition.

4. Answers will vary.

Use It

Answers will vary.

Lesson 15

Take a Closer Look

1. They brought many Spanish words into American English.

2. It has borrowed words from other languages, and other languages have borrowed words from it.

Try It

1. fresh fruit

2. These foods are high in calories, fat, and sodium.

3. fresh fruits

Use It

Answers may vary. Here is an example:

Most of the rules are to keep the pool safe. Rules 7 and 8 are to keep the pool deck clean.

Lesson 16

Take a Closer Look

Answers may vary. Here are some examples:

1. It is not enough information.

2. It goes too far.

3. There is some waste in city departments and civil service agencies, and some workers do not work very hard.

4. It goes too far.

5. Other city workers may share the attitude of the worker who told me to slow down.

Try It

Answers may vary. Here are some examples:

1. It goes too far. Some children may not have been bored.

2. Many of the children seemed bored.

3. It goes too far.

4. I have seen many people ignore or tolerate bad behavior in children.

Use It

Answers will vary.

Lesson 17

Take a Closer Look

Answers will vary.

Try It

Answers will vary.

Use It

Answers will vary.

Lesson 18

Take a Closer Look

1. an atlas

2. a dictionary

3. an encyclopedia

Try It

1. in an atlas

2. in a dictionary

3. in an encyclopedia or an atlas

4. in a world almanac

Use It

Answers may vary. Here are some examples:

"helps you lose weight quickly and keep it off for a lifetime"

"scientifically designed program"

"some of our clients keep eating them even after they've reached their ideal weight"

Lesson 19

Take a Closer Look

1. Music has an essential role in education.

2. Answers will vary.

Try It

1. The music program belongs in the schools.

2. Answers will vary.

Use It

Answers may vary. Here is an example:

The facts given do not prove the case. The writer says what happened with only two children. That is not enough information to make a general statement about all children.

Lesson 20

Take a Closer Look

Answers will vary. Here are some examples:

1. The writer seems to believe that the snacks do not harm children and that the vending machines bring the schools needed money.

2. The writer seems to want to persuade readers that the machines are harmless, or even helpful.

3. The writer seems to want readers to accept the vending machines.

4. If parents agree that the vending machines do not harm children and earn needed money for schools, they may not object to the machines.

Try It

Answers will vary. Here are some examples:

1. The snacks in the machines are inappropriate; the machines should be removed; the board made a poor decision.

2. The writer wants to have the board take the machines out.

3. The writer wants readers to support the position that the board has made a mistake and the machines should be removed.

Use It

Answers will vary.